THE BOTTLECAP SCORE

A Tasting Journal

For Pop Connoisseurs, Soda Jerks, & Soft Drink Enthusiasts

Jason J. Christenson

Illustrated by James W. Christenson

Kayto & Co. Publishing

Minneapolis | Minnesota | USA

THE BOTTLECAP SCORE

A Tasting Journal

For Pop Connoisseurs, Soda Jerks, & Soft Drink Enthusiasts

Jason J. Christenson

Illustrated by James W. Christenson

Kayto & Co. Publishing

Minneapolis | Minnesota | USA

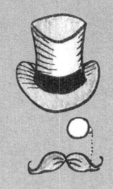

THIS BOOK BELONGS TO:

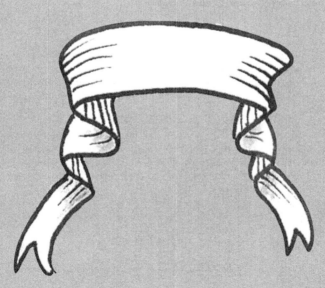

THE BOTTLECAP SCORE
A Tasting Journal for Pop Connoisseurs, Soda Jerks, & Soft Drink Enthusiasts

5105 Oakview Lane North
Plymouth, Minnesota, 55442
www.BottlecapScore.com

Library of Congress Control Number: 2020917755

ISBN-13: 978-1-7327129-5-9

For more information, or to contact the author, please email: contact@BottlecapScore.com

DISCLAIMER & STUFF YOUR DOCTOR MIGHT SAY

When it comes to soda, or any food or drink for that matter, moderation is important. As such, drinking soda should be treated like any desert. Consuming large quantities of soda is not likely to increase your enjoyment for this activity - to the contrary, it is a recipe for a stomach ache. The author and this book assumes that you will take reasonable steps to manage and ensure your own healthy habits. Bottom line: Indulge in these heavenly elixirs responsibly and in moderation!

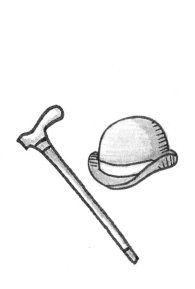

TOASTS

TO MY WONDERFUL, INTELLIGENT, & ENCOURAGING WIFE, BRITTANY. I LOVE YOU.

Also, Special Thanks To:

Alexandra, who will indiscriminately drink any soda loosely associated with a good book.

Brent, whose background as an executive is very evident in the binary decisions to like or dislike the various soda flavors he tries.

Chari, who reconfirmed her assertion that Classic Coca-Cola® from a fountain in a foam cup with ice nuggets is the *only* soda, so far as she is concerned.

Christina, ORT, who is willing to try virtually anything, including soda, at least once (unless it involves spiders).

Cici, Ellie, & Bailey who showed their uncle the importance of marketing by choosing sodas exclusively based upon their packaging aesthetics & the color of the drink.

Dr. Carl, whose attraction to strangely-flavored sodas makes me question whether I want him as my physician.

Dr. Emily, who relates her nastiest, grossest experiences as a veterinarian whilst concurrently sampling various sodas as if it is a normal thing. It's not.

James, my phenomenal illustrator & brother. Also, the man who introduced me to the singularly worst soda I have ever had in my life.

John, whose chemical engineering background & interest in zany flavors has inspired the quantifiable, logical approach in this book. Thank you for all the editing, help, editing, suggestions, editing, encouragement, & editing.

Katie, whose assiduous, sedulous musical approach is only exceeded by her pickiness in soda flavors.

Nathan, who introduced me to the wonderful world of exotic soda.

Nolan, who has only ever found one soda flavor that he's actually disliked.

Pastor Ed, Marylu, & Luke, who always maintain a basement stocked with black cherry & orange soda & kept me well-sugared growing up.

Peter, Esq., the only lawyer who would not sue me for the flavors of soda I have pushed him to try.

Rebecca, a professor who saw an educational opportunity & gave me the idea for this book & upon whom I can always depend to choose safe flavors. Love you, mom.

Scott, who shared a bit of his childhood with his kids & grandkids through soda.

Stephen, who approaches soda tasting with the same gravity he does the millions of dollars he manages. Thanks for the editing help, too!

Tory, who likes soda tasting less for the personal experience & more for the delight in watching others try flavors she knows they will dislike.

Zach, who makes his soda selections exclusively based on intriguing & witty labels.

…And to the many others not mentioned here: Thank you for the memorable times, delicious (& not so delicious) tastes, laughter, & delightful conversation.

MENU OF CONTENTS

INTRODUCTION

Except for my bouncing five-year-old niece at the end of the table, there was a fair amount of good-natured apprehension in the room as the rest of us looked at each other. Each had, at their respective place, a glass containing an ounce of soda. In the center of the table stood a nearly-empty glass bottle, from which the soda had just been poured. This was my niece's selected soda & contribution to the party, purchased earlier in the day. She liked the highlighter-florescent color of the soda that sparkled through the glass bottle. It was advertised as fusion of two dissimilar flavors and, quite frankly, did not sound particularly appetizing.

"Well," I said, "Bottoms up!"

There was a rare moment of silence at the table as everyone lifted their glasses, swished, & swallowed. The groups' collective reaction to the soda was mixed, immediately vocal, & laughable. Spirited & good-natured opinions exploded. Some, like myself, expressed pleasant surprise at the taste, some thought the drink was mediocre & unremarkable, & still others' faces twisted in disgust & horror, swearing the drink was one of the most foul things they had ever tasted.

In today's world it seems hard to find commonality on about anything. Politics, beliefs, backgrounds, professions, age, family dynamics, physical limitations, money, nationality, & many other issues serve to divide or compartmentalize our lives & relationships. Soda tasting is one of those rare activities that can provide ubiquitous enjoyment for everyone, whether by yourself, with a small group or friends, or within a raucous & diverse assembly.

The folks at my table that evening represented an astonishingly diverse mix of people, ages, & professions: a medical doctor, a veterinarian, an attorney, a financial planner, a business executive, a stay-at-home mom, an occupational therapist, an electrical engineering college student, several professional engineers, a professor, a personal trainer, an artist, a musician, retirees, & a swim coach. Moreover, we also had four generations participating at the table, with ages spanning nearly 80 years. Indeed, soda tasting is an activity that everyone & anyone can participate in & enjoy.

This book was written to enable you to start a collection of your own experiences, opinions, & memories. Over the years I have hosted many soda tastings, tried dozens of sodas, & everyone has asked me to do it again. I can promise that the laughter & fun you can have for only a couple of dollars will exceed your expectations! And the hobby only gets more interesting as you find new flavors & brands from the thousands available.

So enjoy your new hobby. Share it with others. Make memories. Become an authoritative soda tasting sommelier. Explore new flavors. Taste new localities. Share a pop with new and old friends. You, & those you bring along with you, are in for a treat!

From my family & friends to yours: Cheers!

PART 1: HOW IT WORKS

THE PART WHERE THE BOTTLECAP SCORE IS EXPLAINED

THE BOTTLECAP SCORE OVERVIEW

Ready to start tasting some sodas? Great! This section will explain how the Bottlecap Score works!

The Bottlecap Score was developed over the course of several years & was designed to evaluate the entire soda experience, not simply the overall taste of the soda. Truly exceptional sodas will float to the top, whereas really poor sodas will sink to the bottom. It will enable you to quantitatively & authoritatively compare various sodas with each other against your tastes, even if a significant amount of time has passed between tastings. It will also provide the soda drinker a more complete framework to objectively & comprehensively evaluate a soda. Your collection of ratings will make you a bona fide expert!

Of course, the ultimate reason that the Bottlecap Score was developed was for the fun you can have! Although the book was designed as a taste-testing journal for one person, the hobby is exponentially more fun to share or experience with other family members & friends who are also rating the same sodas. Whether you consider yourself to be a serious & fanatical soda snob or just a recreational soda drinker, you will find the Bottlecap Score system to be an incredibly fun & enjoyable pastime!

How the Bottlecap Score Works

So how does the Bottlecap Score work? The Bottlecap Score evaluates a soda based upon a 100 point system. Generally, a higher score reflects a soda of superior caliber & character, whereas a lower score denotes a soda with less desirable qualities.

There are ten separate categories upon which each soda is graded. Each of these categories are judged on a scale of zero through ten, with zero being the worst & ten being the best. This means that the highest possible Bottlecap Score can add up to 100 & the lowest possible score is 0 (though it is highly unlikely that you will ever have a perfect-scoring soda or an absolute zero). The Bottlecap Score attempts to weigh all the factors that comprise the entirety of the soda drinking experience. For the Bottlecap Score to work best, the reviewer should try to focus upon each category separately, assigning each category's deserved score.

The Bottlecap Score was designed to judge all soft drinks against each other, not just within a particular flavor group, manufacturer, or specific ingredient makeup. Highly available, well-known, & commercialized sodas can be compared directly against highly localized, much lesser-known, small-batch craft sodas. The most expensive sodas can be compared to the least expensive ones. The highest quality drinks can be compared with the lowest quality drinks. The Bottlecap Score is not biased. Categories or classes of drinks are automatically factored into the Bottlecap Score!

SODA RATINGS

The emoji scale is descriptive of the emotion you feel when determining a rating, & tends to make grading an attribute a bit more approachable & self-explanatory, particularly with younger participants. Unlike most 1-10 scales, a "5" represents a neutral opinion, whereas a "0" represents an extremely negative opinion & a "10" represents your highest, best possible opinion. The following gives some guidance & description of each level of performance:

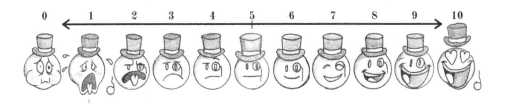

10: Outstanding! Perfect! Magnificent!

The soda's attributes exceed all expectations. To change anything would be to make it a little bit worse. It would definitely represent the top soda for the category. After one sip you take active steps to hide the rest of this magical elixir from anyone else in the house & are considering buying the entire supply from your local supplier. A chorus of angels sings every time you open another bottle. If someone asked you how you liked this soft drink you'd be unable to reply because your mouth is full!

9: Fantastic

A rating of nine means that the soda is as close to perfection as you are yourself! With every marvelous sip you keep saying, "This is delectable!" Your taste buds should be doing little dances around your mouth. If someone asked you how you liked a pop with this rating, you'd probably reply, "This is amazing!" before chugging the rest of the bottle!

8: Delicious

You'll certainly want seconds of this flavorful concoction. It is a solid example of its type & credit to its flavor. The manufacturer did a great job. If someone asked you how you liked a soda with this rating, you'd probably reply, "This is really great!"

17

7: Tasty & Enjoyable

The taste is enjoyable. You would likely buy it again, if offered the chance. While the soda might need a couple small tweaks to perfect it, it is well crafted. It is a credit to the company that makes it & a good representative of its flavor. You know the type: If someone asked you how you liked it, you'd reply, "I like it!"

6: It's Ok

A soda with a rating of six for any category would mean you find it unremarkable, but on the positive side. You probably wouldn't seek out this particular pop again, but you wouldn't be opposed to it if it were handed to you at a party. If someone asked you how you liked it, you'd probably shrug your shoulders & reply, "It's ok."

5: Meh. Take-it-or-leave-it. Neutral.

Rating a soda with a five for any category would mean you find it unremarkable & neutral. Its not bad but it is certainly not good or particularly interesting. With so many better options out there, you probably wouldn't spend money on it again. It is neither good, nor bad. If someone asked you how you liked it, you'd probably shrug your shoulders & reply, "Meh."

4: Improvement Needed

Rating a soda with a four it means that something was off. It's not quite neutral - there is just an element that tips the scales over to a little disquieting or a little gross. You're not angry, just... disappointed. You might be able to see how someone else would like some of its characteristics, but you'd be ok not having this one ever again. Out of politeness, you might be able to choke it down if you had to, just like when your grandmother served steamed vegetables to you as a kid, but it really is not your preference. If someone asked you how you liked the drink, you'd probably frown & shake your head in response.

3: Not Good

The beverage did not live up to its promise. This is a soda which is just plain bad. There may have been interesting elements that had held some promise, but they utterly failed to deliver. You might take a second sip, but only to reconfirm your disgust. You definitely won't finish your glass.

2: Ew, Gross

You cannot help but make a helpless, hurt expression each time this fluid touches your lips. A soda that receives a "two" rating inspires a bit of dread. It's gross. You briefly wonder if you have been the target of some sort of terrible practical joke.

1: Putrid & Nasty

With each sip, a shudder convulses your entire body. You know the feeling - it is the same expression of shock & betrayal that a toddler has when fed a pickle for the first time. It's actually remarkable how awful the stuff is. Your day is ruined & you feel the need to scrape the taste off your tongue & brush your teeth. Just looking at the container causes you to wrinkle your nose in disgust & flee the room.

0: Appalling & Nauseating

Words entirely fail to adequately express your hatred for this repugnant mixture. Rancid bilge water is the kindest way to describe it. It was as if its creators wanted their patrons to get queasy. You will likely use tongs to remove the offending liquid from the premises & bury it in your crabby neighbor's yard. For a category that receives a zero, the soda will have no redeeming quality at all - nothing but concentrated, bottled, liquid dreadful! It is just that horrid.

SCORING CATEGORIES

The Bottlecap Score has ten categories which should be evaluated as independently as possible using the 0-10 scoring system described previously. The order of evaluation is purposeful & is designed to allow as many of the 10 different components to be analyzed independently by the reviewer without the other "upstream" factors negatively or positively influencing "downstream" factors that comprise the totality of the drinking experience. Here are the different categories & some details on the criteria to be evaluated:

Bottle Shape, Style, & Color

This category gives a higher score to those bottlers who make the soda container a part of the fun. Does the container add to your drinking experience? If so, a higher score is warranted. If the bottle does nothing to enhance or detract from your experience, it probably warrants a neutral score of "5." If the container actually detracts from your drinking experience or does not meet the quality of the soda it contains, your score for this category should reflect this. Is the container made of glass, aluminum, plastic, or some other material? Is the shape interesting, different, classic, or unique? Or is the container boring or unattractive? Don't confuse this category with the labeling aesthetics - we are only rating the container itself for this category!

Labeling Aesthetics & Description

This category is fairly self-explanatory. Labels & the drink descriptions that rate highly will be informative or attractive or funny or interesting or witty or even all of the above. Moreover, if the label has any embossing, beautiful coloration, or neat styling, fonts, or artwork, the soda should also rate more highly. There are even labels that change color with temperature! If the label is boring, unattractive, or has little to no information, the Bottlecap Score should be lower. Be careful not to confuse this category with the look of the container or bottle - you have already rated that feature.

Aroma & Drink Color

How does the soda smell? If it has a pleasing effervescence that adds to the flavor or if the scent is distinctive enough to identify the flavor without being overpowering, the soda should score highly. If there is a bitter, chemical, acidic, unidentifiable, or too strong of an odor, the soft drink should receive a lower score.

Additionally, the drink's color is also a factor in this category. Does the color of the soda match your ideal color for the flavor? Does it add to the intrigue of the drink? Is the color as deep or light as you prefer? Depending upon your preferences, a vibrant color may add or detract from your overall experience.

Carbonation / Fizziness

When you first open the bottle, is there a satisfying sound? Does a head of foam appear in the neck of the bottle? Does the drink have the right amount of fizz? A soft drink that is too effervescent for your tastes will receive a lower score. The same is true for a drink that is not bubbly enough. A soda which you think has the perfect amount of carbonation will score highly!

Drinkability / Refreshment

When you drink this soda, does it quench your thirst? Is it a soda that you would choose to drink after some hard work? How easy is it to drink? Would you want to linger over one on the front porch of your grandparent's cabin on a hot day? Is this a beverage that would be easy to finish or will there be a little left over in the bottle when you are done? A drink that forces you to take small sips or brush your teeth immediately afterward will score lower. A soda that leaves you satiated, thirst quenched, & happy - even wanting more - will score highly.

Tastes as Advertised & Expected

Does the soda taste like you expect it to taste? Did it live up to the promise of the labeled flavor? This category can score very highly, even if you don't like the flavor at all. For instance, if you try a Blue Cheese Dressing flavored soda & it tastes exactly like blue cheese, the soda will score highly (regardless if you like it or not!). If, however, you try the concoction & it tastes nothing like you expect it to, then it may score lower, even if you liked the flavor better than you expected.

Overall Flavor

Of course, this is perhaps the most important of all the categories! This is where you record how much you actually enjoyed the soda! How likely are you to drink it again? Did you like the flavor? Did you find the sweetness or tartness of the soft drink at just the right level, or was it too watery or too strong? Could you taste the various ingredients & flavor profiles? Did it have a good bite to it or was it smooth? This is perhaps the most subjective of all the categories - only you know how well you like it!

Aftertaste / Finish

How does the drink finish? Does it cleanse the palette or does it persist? A high scoring soda in this category should leave a short-lived, pleasing flavor in your mouth or throat after you swallow. On the other hand, a lower scoring beverage will leave a nasty or lingering aftertaste, the worst of which will make you want to gargle or gag.

Memorability

This category awards points to soft drinks which will be memorable to you for any reason. Sodas that are classic, nostalgic, novel, represent fun or unusual flavors, or even sodas that are remarkably repugnant and repulsive should all score highly. A beverage that makes you reminisce about tire swings, childhood, hot summer days, & special moments with loved ones will also score highly. A forgettable or uninteresting pop that does not inspire much of a reaction either way will score low.

Value for Price

While most sodas are priced similarly, there are some variations. Your expectations for the soda may change with price, too. For instance, you should expect a soda that costs more than average to taste better than average & vice versa. Did the soda's taste match your expectations for the price you paid? Did it exceed your expectations? If so, rate it higher. Was the soda priced fairly for what you received? Then assign it a neutral "5." If the soda failed to deliver for the price you paid for it, then the rating should be lower. Note: If you are a nerd (like the author) you may find it interesting to include the cost of the soda & where it was purchased in your notes, particularly if you would like to buy that soda again!

The Bottlecap Score

Once you have evaluated all ten different aspects of the soda, add up each of the scores from the ten categories & you will get your final Bottlecap Score!

EXAMPLE SODA EVALUATION

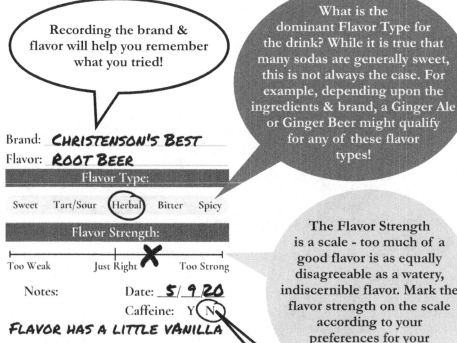

Recording the brand & flavor will help you remember what you tried!

What is the dominant Flavor Type for the drink? While it is true that many sodas are generally sweet, this is not always the case. For example, depending upon the ingredients & brand, a Ginger Ale or Ginger Beer might qualify for any of these flavor types!

Brand: **CHRISTENSON'S BEST**
Flavor: **ROOT BEER**

Flavor Type:

Sweet   Tart/Sour   (Herbal)   Bitter   Spicy

Flavor Strength:

Too Weak   Just Right   Too Strong

The Flavor Strength is a scale - too much of a good flavor is as equally disagreeable as a watery, indiscernible flavor. Mark the flavor strength on the scale according to your preferences for your future reference!

Notes: Date: **5/ 9 20**
Caffeine: Y N

FLAVOR HAS A LITTLE VANILLA IN IT! BOUGHT AT GROCERY FOR $1.50.

Does the soda have caffeine or not? Record it here!

Add your other notes on the sodas, including brief explanations on why & how you rated the drink. If you want, you can also record other details, like where you purchased the soda, ingredients, flavor profiles, where the bottler is based, or how much it cost.

Is the
bottle, cap, can, or
container a neat shape, a cool
color, a unique material or style?
Does it make your drink
experience better?

Is the
labeling
particularly interesting?
Does it compliment the
soda? Is the description
fun, informative, or
beautiful?

Does
the drink have a
pleasing smell?
How do you like
the color of the
soda?

Does
the soda have too
much, too little, or
the perfect amount
of fizz?

Is this the sort of
drink you'd enjoy on a
hot summer day?

Did
the advertised
flavor taste like
it should?

How'd
you like the
flavor?

SODA CHARACTERISTICS	SCORE
Bottle Shape, Style, & Color	3
Labeling Aesthetics & Description	7
Aroma & Drink Color	9
Carbonation / Fizziness	5
Drinkability / Refreshment	6
Tastes as Advertised & Expected	10
Overall Flavor	4
Aftertaste / Finish	8
Memorability	8
Value for Price	8
BOTTLECAP SCORE	68

For good or
bad, was this a
drink you will
remember?

Add all ten
categories
together to get
your Bottlecap
Score for the
soda!

Did the soda leave
a pleasing aftertaste or
did it make you want to
brush your teeth &
gargle?

Was
the price
appropriate for the
value of the
soda?

25

PART 2: SODA TASTING PARTIES

THE PART ABOUT HOSTING THE WORLD'S BEST SODA TASTING PARTY

HOSTING A SODA TASTING PARTY

If you thought tasting & evaluating different brands & flavors of soda was fun on your own, you'll find hosting a soda tasting party is outrageously enjoyable! Whether you invite only one or dozens of friends & family members, it is a great way to spend an afternoon or evening! Using the same Bottlecap Score system, comparing your results can be a highly entertaining experience. You will learn things about your friends or family that you never knew before. An added advantage to inviting a few friends to participate is that you can try a number of different sodas in sequence without wasting any or drinking more than the equivalent of one or two sodas in a sitting!

Your party can be as simple as inviting a few friends or family members over, gathering a variety of sodas, & having some dixie cups or shot glasses, water, & crackers on hand. It can also turn into a regular event, each time focusing on a particular flavor, brand, or theme. There really is no wrong way to host a tasting party - experiment with different ideas & keep things fresh & exciting!

What You Need

A soda tasting party is doesn't require much at all, but your party will be a rollicking success if you gather a few things before it starts. These include:

1-2 SODAS PER PARTICIPANT
Of course, the most important aspect of your soda tasting party is the soda itself! Due to the natural sweetness of the sodas, I like to recommend 1-2 bottles of soda per person.

There are two ways you can procure sodas for your party. First, you can have your invitees bring their own soda to share with the group. Although a duplicate may occur, this approach will reduce the cost to any one person & will generally give you a wide variety of flavors from different stores. If you are privileged to live near a bottler or a specialty soda shop with a wide selection of sodas, it can be doubly fun to go to that store & choose your flavors together! NOTE: To fill in the last category (Value for Price), each purchaser will need to provide the group with cost of the soda(s).

ALLOW TIME TO CHILL

In general, most sodas taste better cold so be sure to allow ample time to chill your sodas before you start your tasting party.

1 CUP PER PARTICIPANT

It should go without saying, but prior to starting your party, gather at least one small cup for each participant for pouring the soda & tasting. Ideally, you want a cup that holds 1-5 ounces of liquid. Shot glasses work very well for this purpose & are usually a very cheap & dishwasher safe, although larger medicine cups, tumblers, or disposable paper bathroom cups are also fantastic options. Alternatively, you can use regular cups, but these make it a little more difficult to meter out the soda appropriately so everyone gets equal amounts.

BOTTLE OPENER

A bottle opener is a must! Without one, your party may come to a frustrating & embarrassing premature end if you cannot get the bottles open! Most glass bottles still require a bottle opener, so don't assume screw-off bottle caps.

SCORESHEET & PEN PER PARTICIPANT

Provide everyone with a **Bottlecap Score Party Evaluation Form** (found on the following page) & a pencil or pen to make notes & rate the various sodas. Feel free to make as many photocopies of the **Bottlecap Score Party Evaluation Form** as you need. Comparing your scores enhances the enjoyment each person will have & leads to funny & animated discussions.

WATER & FOOD

Although optional, the most serious soda enthusiasts may wish to also have a cup of water & some unflavored, dry crackers to cleanse the palate between tastings. A neutral drink or some crackers will prevent the first soda's aftertaste (good or bad) from influencing the next beverage's taste. This is particularly helpful if your flavors are very different & incompatible.

If you want to go all out, a favorite option is a pizza, whether frozen, store-bought, or delivery. Although the flavor of the pizza is strong, it still tends to be a great complementary food because most folks enjoy it, the vast majority of sodas pair well with it, & it is salty which will help keep you & your guests thirsty.

BACKGROUND MUSIC

Another optional, but fun item to have for your party is little background music of your choice. Music always brings a new level of fun to any party!

BOTTLECAP SCORE PARTY EVALUATION SHEET

Name: _____   Date: _____ / _____ / _____

	Brand	Flavor			Brand	Flavor
Soda #1				Soda #5		
Soda #2				Soda #6		
Soda #3				Soda #7		
Soda #4				Soda #8		

SODA CHARACTERISTICS	Soda #1	Soda #2	Soda #3	Soda #4	Soda #5	Soda #6	Soda #7	Soda #8
Bottle Shape, Style, & Color								
Labeling Aesthetics & Description								
Aroma & Drink Color								
Carbonation / Fizziness								
Drinkability / Refreshment								
Tastes as Advertised & Expected								
Overall Flavor								
Aftertaste / Finish								
Memorability								
Value for Price								
BOTTLECAP SCORE								

SODA TASTING PARTY VARIATIONS

Themed Tastings

Soda themes can make any tasting event more interesting. Your theme could focus on a certain types of flavors (like root beers or oranges), certain colors (for instance, red or green), or sampler packs of sodas from a specific brand. Mixing up your party themes will keep the fun interesting for a long time & can really enhance your ability to compare & contrast the individual soda's qualities.

Remote Soda Tasting Party

Remote soda tasting parties take some coordination. Participants at each location must have the same sets of sodas to taste, & the ordering & purchasing of the sodas must be done well in advance of the event. Once the sodas have been received at all locations, schedule an afternoon or evening & use your preferred video chat service (Skype, FaceTime, Zoom, FaceBook, WhatsApp, Google Hangouts, etc.) to taste your soda selections 'together.' This is a great activity, even if you are separated by many miles!

Host a Blind Tasting Party

Blind tastings can be exciting because of the mystery involved. They can also allow the soda enthusiast to evaluate the soda exclusively for its taste - a more objective, uninfluenced assessment to separate the taste of the soda from excellent branding & marketing & all the personal biases for soda that people have developed over the years. The results are often surprising! You'll find that people will prefer brands & flavors they may have never otherwise given a fair try, particularly if you evaluate the same flavor across different brands.

To host a blind taste test, pour the sodas out in matching cups & carefully assign a number to each cup that coordinates with the specific soda. Alternatively, you could wrap each bottle in paper to hide the label. After each person has tasted the soda & rated it & the group has had a chance to compare notes, reveal which number corresponded with which soda. The serious enthusiast can then finish the rating the container, labeling, & price categories.

Visit a Bottler or Specialty Soda Shop

If you are fortunate enough to live near a bottler, many bottlers offer tours of their operations. Taking your tasting party to the location can be an incredible way to spend an hour or two. You may be able to sample a soda right off the line! These tours are usually very interesting, inexpensive, & you will often get to talk to the folks directly responsible for mixing & creating the various flavors. They can tell you much about the experimentation, thought, & effort that goes into developing each & every drink & flavor profile.

PART 3: BEST & WORST SODAS

THE PART WHERE YOU CAN LIST YOUR MOST & LEAST FAVORITE SODAS

33

FAVORITE SODAS LIST

Brand	Flavor	Score	Notes	Page

WORST SODAS LIST

Brand	Flavor	Score	Notes	Page

FAVORITE BRANDS LIST

Brand	Notes	Bottler's Location	Page(s)

BEFORE YOU GO

Thank you!

With so many different forms of entertainment available these days it is such an honor & a delight that you would choose to purchase *The Bottlecap Score*. It is my sincere hope that you've enjoyed this hobby & discovered some new & exciting brands & flavors.

Comments, Suggestions, or Additions?

Got an idea for a later edition? Want to make a suggestion to improve the book? Have a neat story about your experience with *The Bottlecap Score*? Your thoughts, ideas, & stories would be greatly appreciated! Just shoot an email to us at contact@TheBottlecapScore.com. As a very small company, we may not be able to get back to you on all your ideas or suggestions, but know that we read each one!

Please Review!

If you enjoyed this book, would you consider leaving feedback on Amazon.com, your local specialty soda shop, grocery store, or bookseller of choice? I would greatly appreciate it!

Your reviews make *The Bottlecap Score* more visible for those who might not otherwise discover it. Everyone seems to request reviews these days but your thoughts would be more than usually valued. Bonus points to the person with the most clever & fun review!

Cheers!

PART 4: RATING THE SODAS

THE PART WHERE YOU RECORD YOUR BOTTLECAP SCORE REVIEWS

CHERRY FLAVORS

Brand	Flavor	Score	Notes	Page
				41
				41
				42
				42
				43
				43
				44
				44
				45
				45
				46
				46
				47
				47
				48
				48
				49
				49
				50
				50
				51
				51
				52
				52
				53
				53

Brand: _____

Flavor: _____

Flavor Type:

Sweet   Tart/Sour   Herbal   Bitter   Spicy

Flavor Strength:

Too Weak   Just Right   Too Strong

Notes: Date: ___/___/___

Caffeine: Y N

SODA CHARACTERISTICS	SCORE
Bottle Shape, Style, & Color	
Labeling Aesthetics & Description	
Aroma & Drink Color	
Carbonation / Fizziness	
Drinkability / Refreshment	
Tastes as Advertised & Expected	
Overall Flavor	
Aftertaste / Finish	
Memorability	
Value for Price	
BOTTLECAP SCORE	

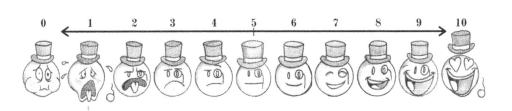

0   1   2   3   4   5   6   7   8   9   10

Brand: _____

Flavor: _____

Flavor Type:

Sweet   Tart/Sour   Herbal   Bitter   Spicy

Flavor Strength:

Too Weak   Just Right   Too Strong

Notes: Date: ___/___/___

Caffeine: Y N

SODA CHARACTERISTICS	SCORE
Bottle Shape, Style, & Color	
Labeling Aesthetics & Description	
Aroma & Drink Color	
Carbonation / Fizziness	
Drinkability / Refreshment	
Tastes as Advertised & Expected	
Overall Flavor	
Aftertaste / Finish	
Memorability	
Value for Price	
BOTTLECAP SCORE	

Brand: _____

Flavor: _____

Flavor Type:
Sweet   Tart/Sour   Herbal   Bitter   Spicy

Flavor Strength:
Too Weak   Just Right   Too Strong

Notes: Date: ___/___/___

Caffeine: Y N

SODA CHARACTERISTICS	SCORE
Bottle Shape, Style, & Color	
Labeling Aesthetics & Description	
Aroma & Drink Color	
Carbonation / Fizziness	
Drinkability / Refreshment	
Tastes as Advertised & Expected	
Overall Flavor	
Aftertaste / Finish	
Memorability	
Value for Price	
BOTTLECAP SCORE	

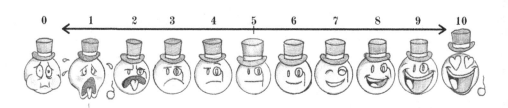

0   1   2   3   4   5   6   7   8   9   10

Brand: _____

Flavor: _____

Flavor Type:
Sweet   Tart/Sour   Herbal   Bitter   Spicy

Flavor Strength:
Too Weak   Just Right   Too Strong

Notes: Date: ___/___/___

Caffeine: Y N

SODA CHARACTERISTICS	SCORE
Bottle Shape, Style, & Color	
Labeling Aesthetics & Description	
Aroma & Drink Color	
Carbonation / Fizziness	
Drinkability / Refreshment	
Tastes as Advertised & Expected	
Overall Flavor	
Aftertaste / Finish	
Memorability	
Value for Price	
BOTTLECAP SCORE	

Brand: _____

Flavor: _____

Flavor Type:

Sweet   Tart/Sour   Herbal   Bitter   Spicy

Flavor Strength:

Too Weak   Just Right   Too Strong

Notes: Date: ___/___/___

              Caffeine: Y N

SODA CHARACTERISTICS	SCORE
Bottle Shape, Style, & Color	
Labeling Aesthetics & Description	
Aroma & Drink Color	
Carbonation / Fizziness	
Drinkability / Refreshment	
Tastes as Advertised & Expected	
Overall Flavor	
Aftertaste / Finish	
Memorability	
Value for Price	
BOTTLECAP SCORE	

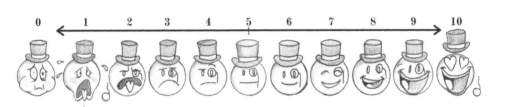

0   1   2   3   4   5   6   7   8   9   10

Brand: _____

Flavor: _____

Flavor Type:

Sweet   Tart/Sour   Herbal   Bitter   Spicy

Flavor Strength:

Too Weak   Just Right   Too Strong

Notes: Date: ___/___/___

              Caffeine: Y N

SODA CHARACTERISTICS	SCORE
Bottle Shape, Style, & Color	
Labeling Aesthetics & Description	
Aroma & Drink Color	
Carbonation / Fizziness	
Drinkability / Refreshment	
Tastes as Advertised & Expected	
Overall Flavor	
Aftertaste / Finish	
Memorability	
Value for Price	
BOTTLECAP SCORE	

Brand: _____

Flavor: _____

Flavor Type:
Sweet   Tart/Sour   Herbal   Bitter   Spicy

Flavor Strength:

Too Weak   Just Right   Too Strong

Notes: Date: ___/___/___

Caffeine: Y N

SODA CHARACTERISTICS	SCORE
Bottle Shape, Style, & Color	
Labeling Aesthetics & Description	
Aroma & Drink Color	
Carbonation / Fizziness	
Drinkability / Refreshment	
Tastes as Advertised & Expected	
Overall Flavor	
Aftertaste / Finish	
Memorability	
Value for Price	
BOTTLECAP SCORE	

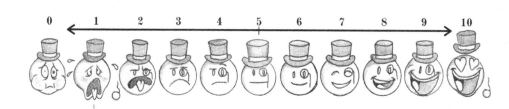

0   1   2   3   4   5   6   7   8   9   10

Brand: _____

Flavor: _____

Flavor Type:
Sweet   Tart/Sour   Herbal   Bitter   Spicy

Flavor Strength:

Too Weak   Just Right   Too Strong

Notes: Date: ___/___/___

Caffeine: Y N

SODA CHARACTERISTICS	SCORE
Bottle Shape, Style, & Color	
Labeling Aesthetics & Description	
Aroma & Drink Color	
Carbonation / Fizziness	
Drinkability / Refreshment	
Tastes as Advertised & Expected	
Overall Flavor	
Aftertaste / Finish	
Memorability	
Value for Price	
BOTTLECAP SCORE	

Brand: _____

Flavor: _____

Flavor Type:				
Sweet	Tart/Sour	Herbal	Bitter	Spicy

Flavor Strength:
Too Weak   Just Right   Too Strong

Notes: Date: ___/___/___

Caffeine: Y N

SODA CHARACTERISTICS	SCORE
Bottle Shape, Style, & Color	
Labeling Aesthetics & Description	
Aroma & Drink Color	
Carbonation / Fizziness	
Drinkability / Refreshment	
Tastes as Advertised & Expected	
Overall Flavor	
Aftertaste / Finish	
Memorability	
Value for Price	
BOTTLECAP SCORE	

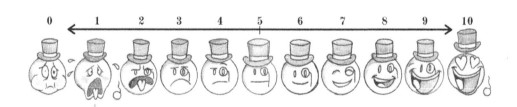

Brand: _____

Flavor: _____

Flavor Type:				
Sweet	Tart/Sour	Herbal	Bitter	Spicy

Flavor Strength:
Too Weak   Just Right   Too Strong

Notes: Date: ___/___/___

Caffeine: Y N

SODA CHARACTERISTICS	SCORE
Bottle Shape, Style, & Color	
Labeling Aesthetics & Description	
Aroma & Drink Color	
Carbonation / Fizziness	
Drinkability / Refreshment	
Tastes as Advertised & Expected	
Overall Flavor	
Aftertaste / Finish	
Memorability	
Value for Price	
BOTTLECAP SCORE	

Brand: _____

Flavor: _____

Flavor Type:

Sweet   Tart/Sour   Herbal   Bitter   Spicy

Flavor Strength:

Too Weak   Just Right   Too Strong

Notes: Date: ___/___/___

Caffeine: Y N

SODA CHARACTERISTICS	SCORE
Bottle Shape, Style, & Color	
Labeling Aesthetics & Description	
Aroma & Drink Color	
Carbonation / Fizziness	
Drinkability / Refreshment	
Tastes as Advertised & Expected	
Overall Flavor	
Aftertaste / Finish	
Memorability	
Value for Price	
BOTTLECAP SCORE	

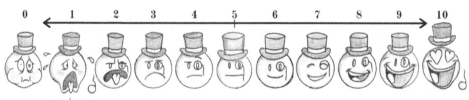

0   1   2   3   4   5   6   7   8   9   10

Brand: _____

Flavor: _____

Flavor Type:

Sweet   Tart/Sour   Herbal   Bitter   Spicy

Flavor Strength:

Too Weak   Just Right   Too Strong

Notes: Date: ___/___/___

Caffeine: Y N

SODA CHARACTERISTICS	SCORE
Bottle Shape, Style, & Color	
Labeling Aesthetics & Description	
Aroma & Drink Color	
Carbonation / Fizziness	
Drinkability / Refreshment	
Tastes as Advertised & Expected	
Overall Flavor	
Aftertaste / Finish	
Memorability	
Value for Price	
BOTTLECAP SCORE	

Brand: _____

Flavor: _____

Flavor Type:				
Sweet	Tart/Sour	Herbal	Bitter	Spicy

Flavor Strength:

Too Weak — Just Right — Too Strong

Notes:

Date: ___/___/___

Caffeine: Y N

SODA CHARACTERISTICS	SCORE
Bottle Shape, Style, & Color	
Labeling Aesthetics & Description	
Aroma & Drink Color	
Carbonation / Fizziness	
Drinkability / Refreshment	
Tastes as Advertised & Expected	
Overall Flavor	
Aftertaste / Finish	
Memorability	
Value for Price	
BOTTLECAP SCORE	

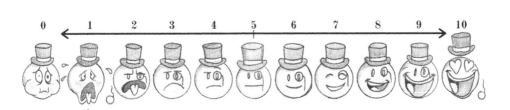

Brand: _____

Flavor: _____

Flavor Type:				
Sweet	Tart/Sour	Herbal	Bitter	Spicy

Flavor Strength:

Too Weak — Just Right — Too Strong

Notes:

Date: ___/___/___

Caffeine: Y N

SODA CHARACTERISTICS	SCORE
Bottle Shape, Style, & Color	
Labeling Aesthetics & Description	
Aroma & Drink Color	
Carbonation / Fizziness	
Drinkability / Refreshment	
Tastes as Advertised & Expected	
Overall Flavor	
Aftertaste / Finish	
Memorability	
Value for Price	
BOTTLECAP SCORE	

Brand: _____

Flavor: _____

Flavor Type:				
Sweet	Tart/Sour	Herbal	Bitter	Spicy

Flavor Strength:

Too Weak   Just Right   Too Strong

Notes: Date: ___/___/___

Caffeine: Y N

SODA CHARACTERISTICS	SCORE
Bottle Shape, Style, & Color	
Labeling Aesthetics & Description	
Aroma & Drink Color	
Carbonation / Fizziness	
Drinkability / Refreshment	
Tastes as Advertised & Expected	
Overall Flavor	
Aftertaste / Finish	
Memorability	
Value for Price	
BOTTLECAP SCORE	

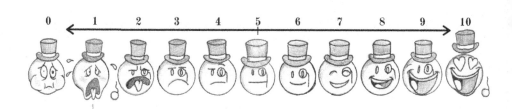

0   1   2   3   4   5   6   7   8   9   10

Brand: _____

Flavor: _____

Flavor Type:				
Sweet	Tart/Sour	Herbal	Bitter	Spicy

Flavor Strength:

Too Weak   Just Right   Too Strong

Notes: Date: ___/___/___

Caffeine: Y N

SODA CHARACTERISTICS	SCORE
Bottle Shape, Style, & Color	
Labeling Aesthetics & Description	
Aroma & Drink Color	
Carbonation / Fizziness	
Drinkability / Refreshment	
Tastes as Advertised & Expected	
Overall Flavor	
Aftertaste / Finish	
Memorability	
Value for Price	
BOTTLECAP SCORE	

Brand: _____

Flavor: _____

Flavor Type:				
Sweet	Tart/Sour	Herbal	Bitter	Spicy

Flavor Strength:

Too Weak   Just Right   Too Strong

Notes: Date: ___/___/___

Caffeine: Y N

SODA CHARACTERISTICS	SCORE
Bottle Shape, Style, & Color	
Labeling Aesthetics & Description	
Aroma & Drink Color	
Carbonation / Fizziness	
Drinkability / Refreshment	
Tastes as Advertised & Expected	
Overall Flavor	
Aftertaste / Finish	
Memorability	
Value for Price	
BOTTLECAP SCORE	

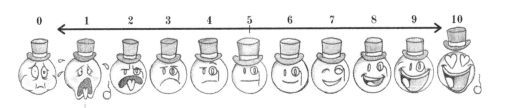

0   1   2   3   4   5   6   7   8   9   10

Brand: _____

Flavor: _____

Flavor Type:				
Sweet	Tart/Sour	Herbal	Bitter	Spicy

Flavor Strength:

Too Weak   Just Right   Too Strong

Notes: Date: ___/___/___

Caffeine: Y N

SODA CHARACTERISTICS	SCORE
Bottle Shape, Style, & Color	
Labeling Aesthetics & Description	
Aroma & Drink Color	
Carbonation / Fizziness	
Drinkability / Refreshment	
Tastes as Advertised & Expected	
Overall Flavor	
Aftertaste / Finish	
Memorability	
Value for Price	
BOTTLECAP SCORE	

Brand: _____

Flavor: _____

SODA CHARACTERISTICS	SCORE
Bottle Shape, Style, & Color	
Labeling Aesthetics & Description	
Aroma & Drink Color	
Carbonation / Fizziness	
Drinkability / Refreshment	
Tastes as Advertised & Expected	
Overall Flavor	
Aftertaste / Finish	
Memorability	
Value for Price	
BOTTLECAP SCORE	

Flavor Type:

Sweet   Tart/Sour   Herbal   Bitter   Spicy

Flavor Strength:

Too Weak   Just Right   Too Strong

Notes: Date: ___/___/___

Caffeine: Y N

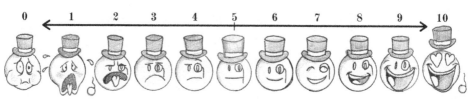

| 0 | 1 | 2 | 3 | 4 | 5 | 6 | 7 | 8 | 9 | 10 |

Brand: _____

Flavor: _____

SODA CHARACTERISTICS	SCORE
Bottle Shape, Style, & Color	
Labeling Aesthetics & Description	
Aroma & Drink Color	
Carbonation / Fizziness	
Drinkability / Refreshment	
Tastes as Advertised & Expected	
Overall Flavor	
Aftertaste / Finish	
Memorability	
Value for Price	
BOTTLECAP SCORE	

Flavor Type:

Sweet   Tart/Sour   Herbal   Bitter   Spicy

Flavor Strength:

Too Weak   Just Right   Too Strong

Notes: Date: ___/___/___

Caffeine: Y N

Brand: _____

Flavor: _____

Flavor Type:				
Sweet	Tart/Sour	Herbal	Bitter	Spicy

Flavor Strength:

Too Weak — Just Right — Too Strong

Notes:

Date: ___/___/___

Caffeine: Y   N

SODA CHARACTERISTICS	SCORE
Bottle Shape, Style, & Color	
Labeling Aesthetics & Description	
Aroma & Drink Color	
Carbonation / Fizziness	
Drinkability / Refreshment	
Tastes as Advertised & Expected	
Overall Flavor	
Aftertaste / Finish	
Memorability	
Value for Price	
BOTTLECAP SCORE	

0   1   2   3   4   5   6   7   8   9   10

Brand: _____

Flavor: _____

Flavor Type:				
Sweet	Tart/Sour	Herbal	Bitter	Spicy

Flavor Strength:

Too Weak — Just Right — Too Strong

Notes:

Date: ___/___/___

Caffeine: Y   N

SODA CHARACTERISTICS	SCORE
Bottle Shape, Style, & Color	
Labeling Aesthetics & Description	
Aroma & Drink Color	
Carbonation / Fizziness	
Drinkability / Refreshment	
Tastes as Advertised & Expected	
Overall Flavor	
Aftertaste / Finish	
Memorability	
Value for Price	
BOTTLECAP SCORE	

Brand: _____

Flavor: _____

Flavor Type:

Sweet   Tart/Sour   Herbal   Bitter   Spicy

Flavor Strength:

Too Weak   Just Right   Too Strong

Notes: Date: ___/___/___

Caffeine: Y N

SODA CHARACTERISTICS	SCORE
Bottle Shape, Style, & Color	
Labeling Aesthetics & Description	
Aroma & Drink Color	
Carbonation / Fizziness	
Drinkability / Refreshment	
Tastes as Advertised & Expected	
Overall Flavor	
Aftertaste / Finish	
Memorability	
Value for Price	
BOTTLECAP SCORE	

0   1   2   3   4   5   6   7   8   9   10

Brand: _____

Flavor: _____

Flavor Type:

Sweet   Tart/Sour   Herbal   Bitter   Spicy

Flavor Strength:

Too Weak   Just Right   Too Strong

Notes: Date: ___/___/___

Caffeine: Y N

SODA CHARACTERISTICS	SCORE
Bottle Shape, Style, & Color	
Labeling Aesthetics & Description	
Aroma & Drink Color	
Carbonation / Fizziness	
Drinkability / Refreshment	
Tastes as Advertised & Expected	
Overall Flavor	
Aftertaste / Finish	
Memorability	
Value for Price	
BOTTLECAP SCORE	

Brand: _____

Flavor: _____

Flavor Type:

Sweet   Tart/Sour   Herbal   Bitter   Spicy

Flavor Strength:

Too Weak   Just Right   Too Strong

Notes: Date: ___/___/___

Caffeine: Y   N

SODA CHARACTERISTICS	SCORE
Bottle Shape, Style, & Color	
Labeling Aesthetics & Description	
Aroma & Drink Color	
Carbonation / Fizziness	
Drinkability / Refreshment	
Tastes as Advertised & Expected	
Overall Flavor	
Aftertaste / Finish	
Memorability	
Value for Price	
BOTTLECAP SCORE	

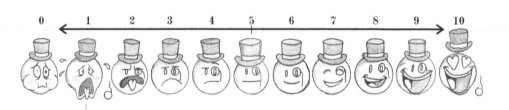

0   1   2   3   4   5   6   7   8   9   10

Brand: _____

Flavor: _____

Flavor Type:

Sweet   Tart/Sour   Herbal   Bitter   Spicy

Flavor Strength:

Too Weak   Just Right   Too Strong

Notes: Date: ___/___/___

Caffeine: Y   N

SODA CHARACTERISTICS	SCORE
Bottle Shape, Style, & Color	
Labeling Aesthetics & Description	
Aroma & Drink Color	
Carbonation / Fizziness	
Drinkability / Refreshment	
Tastes as Advertised & Expected	
Overall Flavor	
Aftertaste / Finish	
Memorability	
Value for Price	
BOTTLECAP SCORE	

CITRUS FLAVORS

DOES NOT INCLUDE ORANGE, LEMON, OR LIME FLAVORS

Brand	Flavor	Score	Notes	Page
				55
				55
				56
				56
				57
				57
				58
				58
				59
				59
				60
				60
				61
				61
				62
				62
				63
				63
				64
				64
				65
				65
				66
				66
				67
				67

Brand: _____

Flavor: _____

Flavor Type:

Sweet　　Tart/Sour　　Herbal　　Bitter　　Spicy

Flavor Strength:

Too Weak　　Just Right　　Too Strong

Notes:　　Date: ___/___/___

Caffeine:　Y　N

SODA CHARACTERISTICS	SCORE
Bottle Shape, Style, & Color	
Labeling Aesthetics & Description	
Aroma & Drink Color	
Carbonation / Fizziness	
Drinkability / Refreshment	
Tastes as Advertised & Expected	
Overall Flavor	
Aftertaste / Finish	
Memorability	
Value for Price	
BOTTLECAP SCORE	

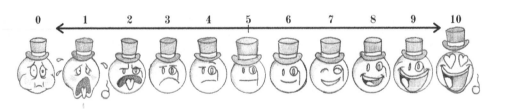

0　1　2　3　4　5　6　7　8　9　10

Brand: _____

Flavor: _____

Flavor Type:

Sweet　　Tart/Sour　　Herbal　　Bitter　　Spicy

Flavor Strength:

Too Weak　　Just Right　　Too Strong

Notes:　　Date: ___/___/___

Caffeine:　Y　N

SODA CHARACTERISTICS	SCORE
Bottle Shape, Style, & Color	
Labeling Aesthetics & Description	
Aroma & Drink Color	
Carbonation / Fizziness	
Drinkability / Refreshment	
Tastes as Advertised & Expected	
Overall Flavor	
Aftertaste / Finish	
Memorability	
Value for Price	
BOTTLECAP SCORE	

Brand: _____

Flavor: _____

Flavor Type:

Sweet   Tart/Sour   Herbal   Bitter   Spicy

Flavor Strength:

Too Weak   Just Right   Too Strong

Notes: Date: ___/___/___

Caffeine: Y   N

SODA CHARACTERISTICS	SCORE
Bottle Shape, Style, & Color	
Labeling Aesthetics & Description	
Aroma & Drink Color	
Carbonation / Fizziness	
Drinkability / Refreshment	
Tastes as Advertised & Expected	
Overall Flavor	
Aftertaste / Finish	
Memorability	
Value for Price	
BOTTLECAP SCORE	

0   1   2   3   4   5   6   7   8   9   10

Brand: _____

Flavor: _____

Flavor Type:

Sweet   Tart/Sour   Herbal   Bitter   Spicy

Flavor Strength:

Too Weak   Just Right   Too Strong

Notes: Date: ___/___/___

Caffeine: Y   N

SODA CHARACTERISTICS	SCORE
Bottle Shape, Style, & Color	
Labeling Aesthetics & Description	
Aroma & Drink Color	
Carbonation / Fizziness	
Drinkability / Refreshment	
Tastes as Advertised & Expected	
Overall Flavor	
Aftertaste / Finish	
Memorability	
Value for Price	
BOTTLECAP SCORE	

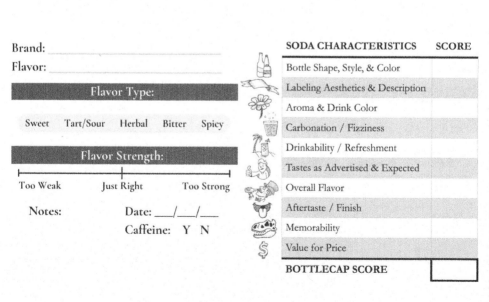

Brand: _____

Flavor: _____

Flavor Type:				
Sweet	Tart/Sour	Herbal	Bitter	Spicy

Flavor Strength:

Too Weak　　　Just Right　　　Too Strong

Notes:　　　Date: ___/___/___

Caffeine: Y N

SODA CHARACTERISTICS	SCORE
Bottle Shape, Style, & Color	
Labeling Aesthetics & Description	
Aroma & Drink Color	
Carbonation / Fizziness	
Drinkability / Refreshment	
Tastes as Advertised & Expected	
Overall Flavor	
Aftertaste / Finish	
Memorability	
Value for Price	
BOTTLECAP SCORE	

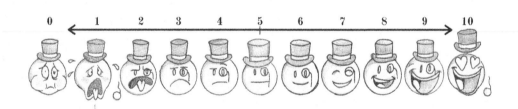

Brand: _____

Flavor: _____

Flavor Type:				
Sweet	Tart/Sour	Herbal	Bitter	Spicy

Flavor Strength:

Too Weak　　　Just Right　　　Too Strong

Notes:　　　Date: ___/___/___

Caffeine: Y N

SODA CHARACTERISTICS	SCORE
Bottle Shape, Style, & Color	
Labeling Aesthetics & Description	
Aroma & Drink Color	
Carbonation / Fizziness	
Drinkability / Refreshment	
Tastes as Advertised & Expected	
Overall Flavor	
Aftertaste / Finish	
Memorability	
Value for Price	
BOTTLECAP SCORE	

Brand: _____

Flavor: _____

Flavor Type:

Sweet   Tart/Sour   Herbal   Bitter   Spicy

Flavor Strength:

Too Weak   Just Right   Too Strong

Notes: Date: ___/___/___

Caffeine: Y N

SODA CHARACTERISTICS	SCORE
Bottle Shape, Style, & Color	
Labeling Aesthetics & Description	
Aroma & Drink Color	
Carbonation / Fizziness	
Drinkability / Refreshment	
Tastes as Advertised & Expected	
Overall Flavor	
Aftertaste / Finish	
Memorability	
Value for Price	
BOTTLECAP SCORE	

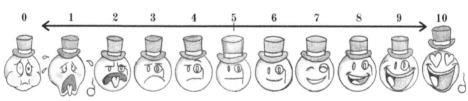

0   1   2   3   4   5   6   7   8   9   10

Brand: _____

Flavor: _____

Flavor Type:

Sweet   Tart/Sour   Herbal   Bitter   Spicy

Flavor Strength:

Too Weak   Just Right   Too Strong

Notes: Date: ___/___/___

Caffeine: Y N

SODA CHARACTERISTICS	SCORE
Bottle Shape, Style, & Color	
Labeling Aesthetics & Description	
Aroma & Drink Color	
Carbonation / Fizziness	
Drinkability / Refreshment	
Tastes as Advertised & Expected	
Overall Flavor	
Aftertaste / Finish	
Memorability	
Value for Price	
BOTTLECAP SCORE	

Brand: _____

Flavor: _____

SODA CHARACTERISTICS	SCORE
Bottle Shape, Style, & Color	
Labeling Aesthetics & Description	
Aroma & Drink Color	
Carbonation / Fizziness	
Drinkability / Refreshment	
Tastes as Advertised & Expected	
Overall Flavor	
Aftertaste / Finish	
Memorability	
Value for Price	
BOTTLECAP SCORE	

Flavor Type:

Sweet　　Tart/Sour　　Herbal　　Bitter　　Spicy

Flavor Strength:

Too Weak　　Just Right　　Too Strong

Notes:　　Date: ___/___/___

Caffeine:　Y　N

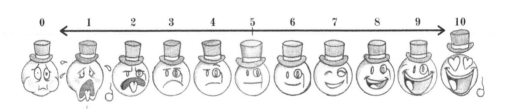

Brand: _____

Flavor: _____

SODA CHARACTERISTICS	SCORE
Bottle Shape, Style, & Color	
Labeling Aesthetics & Description	
Aroma & Drink Color	
Carbonation / Fizziness	
Drinkability / Refreshment	
Tastes as Advertised & Expected	
Overall Flavor	
Aftertaste / Finish	
Memorability	
Value for Price	
BOTTLECAP SCORE	

Flavor Type:

Sweet　　Tart/Sour　　Herbal　　Bitter　　Spicy

Flavor Strength:

Too Weak　　Just Right　　Too Strong

Notes:　　Date: ___/___/___

Caffeine:　Y　N

Brand: _____

Flavor: _____

Flavor Type:

Sweet   Tart/Sour   Herbal   Bitter   Spicy

Flavor Strength:

Too Weak   Just Right   Too Strong

Notes: Date: ___/___/___

Caffeine: Y N

SODA CHARACTERISTICS	SCORE
Bottle Shape, Style, & Color	
Labeling Aesthetics & Description	
Aroma & Drink Color	
Carbonation / Fizziness	
Drinkability / Refreshment	
Tastes as Advertised & Expected	
Overall Flavor	
Aftertaste / Finish	
Memorability	
Value for Price	
BOTTLECAP SCORE	

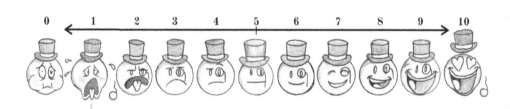

0   1   2   3   4   5   6   7   8   9   10

Brand: _____

Flavor: _____

Flavor Type:

Sweet   Tart/Sour   Herbal   Bitter   Spicy

Flavor Strength:

Too Weak   Just Right   Too Strong

Notes: Date: ___/___/___

Caffeine: Y N

SODA CHARACTERISTICS	SCORE
Bottle Shape, Style, & Color	
Labeling Aesthetics & Description	
Aroma & Drink Color	
Carbonation / Fizziness	
Drinkability / Refreshment	
Tastes as Advertised & Expected	
Overall Flavor	
Aftertaste / Finish	
Memorability	
Value for Price	
BOTTLECAP SCORE	

Brand: _____

Flavor: _____

Flavor Type:				
Sweet	Tart/Sour	Herbal	Bitter	Spicy

Flavor Strength:

Too Weak   Just Right   Too Strong

Notes: Date: ___/___/___

Caffeine: Y N

SODA CHARACTERISTICS	SCORE
Bottle Shape, Style, & Color	
Labeling Aesthetics & Description	
Aroma & Drink Color	
Carbonation / Fizziness	
Drinkability / Refreshment	
Tastes as Advertised & Expected	
Overall Flavor	
Aftertaste / Finish	
Memorability	
Value for Price	
BOTTLECAP SCORE	

| 0 | 1 | 2 | 3 | 4 | 5 | 6 | 7 | 8 | 9 | 10 |

Brand: _____

Flavor: _____

Flavor Type:				
Sweet	Tart/Sour	Herbal	Bitter	Spicy

Flavor Strength:

Too Weak   Just Right   Too Strong

Notes: Date: ___/___/___

Caffeine: Y N

SODA CHARACTERISTICS	SCORE
Bottle Shape, Style, & Color	
Labeling Aesthetics & Description	
Aroma & Drink Color	
Carbonation / Fizziness	
Drinkability / Refreshment	
Tastes as Advertised & Expected	
Overall Flavor	
Aftertaste / Finish	
Memorability	
Value for Price	
BOTTLECAP SCORE	

Brand: _____

Flavor: _____

Flavor Type:

Sweet   Tart/Sour   Herbal   Bitter   Spicy

Flavor Strength:

Too Weak   Just Right   Too Strong

Notes: Date: ___/___/___

Caffeine: Y   N

SODA CHARACTERISTICS	SCORE
Bottle Shape, Style, & Color	
Labeling Aesthetics & Description	
Aroma & Drink Color	
Carbonation / Fizziness	
Drinkability / Refreshment	
Tastes as Advertised & Expected	
Overall Flavor	
Aftertaste / Finish	
Memorability	
Value for Price	
BOTTLECAP SCORE	

Brand: _____

Flavor: _____

Flavor Type:

Sweet   Tart/Sour   Herbal   Bitter   Spicy

Flavor Strength:

Too Weak   Just Right   Too Strong

Notes: Date: ___/___/___

Caffeine: Y   N

SODA CHARACTERISTICS	SCORE
Bottle Shape, Style, & Color	
Labeling Aesthetics & Description	
Aroma & Drink Color	
Carbonation / Fizziness	
Drinkability / Refreshment	
Tastes as Advertised & Expected	
Overall Flavor	
Aftertaste / Finish	
Memorability	
Value for Price	
BOTTLECAP SCORE	

Brand: _____

Flavor: _____

Flavor Type:

Sweet   Tart/Sour   Herbal   Bitter   Spicy

Flavor Strength:

Too Weak   Just Right   Too Strong

Notes: Date: ___/___/___

                Caffeine: Y N

SODA CHARACTERISTICS	SCORE
Bottle Shape, Style, & Color	
Labeling Aesthetics & Description	
Aroma & Drink Color	
Carbonation / Fizziness	
Drinkability / Refreshment	
Tastes as Advertised & Expected	
Overall Flavor	
Aftertaste / Finish	
Memorability	
Value for Price	
BOTTLECAP SCORE	

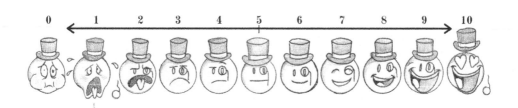

0   1   2   3   4   5   6   7   8   9   10

Brand: _____

Flavor: _____

Flavor Type:

Sweet   Tart/Sour   Herbal   Bitter   Spicy

Flavor Strength:

Too Weak   Just Right   Too Strong

Notes: Date: ___/___/___

                Caffeine: Y N

SODA CHARACTERISTICS	SCORE
Bottle Shape, Style, & Color	
Labeling Aesthetics & Description	
Aroma & Drink Color	
Carbonation / Fizziness	
Drinkability / Refreshment	
Tastes as Advertised & Expected	
Overall Flavor	
Aftertaste / Finish	
Memorability	
Value for Price	
BOTTLECAP SCORE	

Brand: _____

Flavor: _____

Flavor Type:

Sweet   Tart/Sour   Herbal   Bitter   Spicy

Flavor Strength:

Too Weak   Just Right   Too Strong

Notes: Date: ___/___/___

Caffeine: Y N

SODA CHARACTERISTICS	SCORE
Bottle Shape, Style, & Color	
Labeling Aesthetics & Description	
Aroma & Drink Color	
Carbonation / Fizziness	
Drinkability / Refreshment	
Tastes as Advertised & Expected	
Overall Flavor	
Aftertaste / Finish	
Memorability	
Value for Price	
BOTTLECAP SCORE	

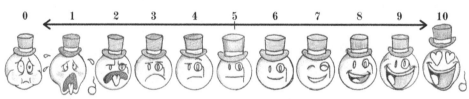

0   1   2   3   4   5   6   7   8   9   10

Brand: _____

Flavor: _____

Flavor Type:

Sweet   Tart/Sour   Herbal   Bitter   Spicy

Flavor Strength:

Too Weak   Just Right   Too Strong

Notes: Date: ___/___/___

Caffeine: Y N

SODA CHARACTERISTICS	SCORE
Bottle Shape, Style, & Color	
Labeling Aesthetics & Description	
Aroma & Drink Color	
Carbonation / Fizziness	
Drinkability / Refreshment	
Tastes as Advertised & Expected	
Overall Flavor	
Aftertaste / Finish	
Memorability	
Value for Price	
BOTTLECAP SCORE	

Brand: _____

Flavor: _____

SODA CHARACTERISTICS	SCORE
Bottle Shape, Style, & Color	

Flavor Type:

Sweet	Tart/Sour	Herbal	Bitter	Spicy

SODA CHARACTERISTICS	SCORE
Labeling Aesthetics & Description	
Aroma & Drink Color	
Carbonation / Fizziness	
Drinkability / Refreshment	
Tastes as Advertised & Expected	
Overall Flavor	
Aftertaste / Finish	
Memorability	
Value for Price	
BOTTLECAP SCORE	

Flavor Strength:

Too Weak	Just Right	Too Strong

Notes:

Date: ___/___/___

Caffeine: Y N

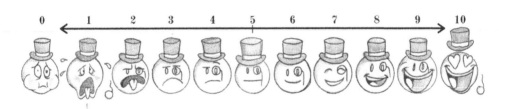

Brand: _____

Flavor: _____

SODA CHARACTERISTICS	SCORE
Bottle Shape, Style, & Color	

Flavor Type:

Sweet	Tart/Sour	Herbal	Bitter	Spicy

SODA CHARACTERISTICS	SCORE
Labeling Aesthetics & Description	
Aroma & Drink Color	
Carbonation / Fizziness	
Drinkability / Refreshment	
Tastes as Advertised & Expected	
Overall Flavor	
Aftertaste / Finish	
Memorability	
Value for Price	
BOTTLECAP SCORE	

Flavor Strength:

Too Weak	Just Right	Too Strong

Notes:

Date: ___/___/___

Caffeine: Y N

Brand: _____

Flavor: _____

Flavor Type:

Sweet   Tart/Sour   Herbal   Bitter   Spicy

Flavor Strength:

Too Weak   Just Right   Too Strong

Notes: Date: ___/___/___

Caffeine: Y N

SODA CHARACTERISTICS	SCORE
Bottle Shape, Style, & Color	
Labeling Aesthetics & Description	
Aroma & Drink Color	
Carbonation / Fizziness	
Drinkability / Refreshment	
Tastes as Advertised & Expected	
Overall Flavor	
Aftertaste / Finish	
Memorability	
Value for Price	
BOTTLECAP SCORE	

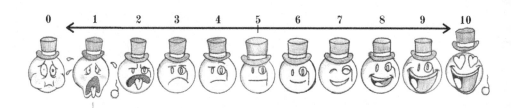

0 1 2 3 4 5 6 7 8 9 10

Brand: _____

Flavor: _____

Flavor Type:

Sweet   Tart/Sour   Herbal   Bitter   Spicy

Flavor Strength:

Too Weak   Just Right   Too Strong

Notes: Date: ___/___/___

Caffeine: Y N

SODA CHARACTERISTICS	SCORE
Bottle Shape, Style, & Color	
Labeling Aesthetics & Description	
Aroma & Drink Color	
Carbonation / Fizziness	
Drinkability / Refreshment	
Tastes as Advertised & Expected	
Overall Flavor	
Aftertaste / Finish	
Memorability	
Value for Price	
BOTTLECAP SCORE	

Brand: _____

Flavor: _____

Flavor Type:

Sweet   Tart/Sour   Herbal   Bitter   Spicy

Flavor Strength:

Too Weak   Just Right   Too Strong

Notes: Date: ___/___/___

Caffeine: Y N

SODA CHARACTERISTICS	SCORE
Bottle Shape, Style, & Color	
Labeling Aesthetics & Description	
Aroma & Drink Color	
Carbonation / Fizziness	
Drinkability / Refreshment	
Tastes as Advertised & Expected	
Overall Flavor	
Aftertaste / Finish	
Memorability	
Value for Price	
BOTTLECAP SCORE	

0   1   2   3   4   5   6   7   8   9   10

Brand: _____

Flavor: _____

Flavor Type:

Sweet   Tart/Sour   Herbal   Bitter   Spicy

Flavor Strength:

Too Weak   Just Right   Too Strong

Notes: Date: ___/___/___

Caffeine: Y N

SODA CHARACTERISTICS	SCORE
Bottle Shape, Style, & Color	
Labeling Aesthetics & Description	
Aroma & Drink Color	
Carbonation / Fizziness	
Drinkability / Refreshment	
Tastes as Advertised & Expected	
Overall Flavor	
Aftertaste / Finish	
Memorability	
Value for Price	
BOTTLECAP SCORE	

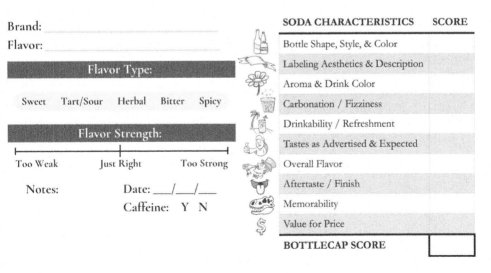

COLA FLAVORS

Brand	Flavor	Score	Notes	Page
				69
				69
				70
				70
				71
				71
				72
				72
				73
				73
				74
				74
				75
				75
				76
				76
				77
				77
				78
				78
				79
				79
				80
				80
				81
				81

Brand: _____

Flavor: _____

Flavor Type:

Sweet Tart/Sour Herbal Bitter Spicy

Flavor Strength:

Too Weak   Just Right   Too Strong

Notes: Date: ___/___/___

Caffeine: Y N

SODA CHARACTERISTICS	SCORE
Bottle Shape, Style, & Color	
Labeling Aesthetics & Description	
Aroma & Drink Color	
Carbonation / Fizziness	
Drinkability / Refreshment	
Tastes as Advertised & Expected	
Overall Flavor	
Aftertaste / Finish	
Memorability	
Value for Price	
BOTTLECAP SCORE	

0 1 2 3 4 5 6 7 8 9 10

Brand: _____

Flavor: _____

Flavor Type:

Sweet Tart/Sour Herbal Bitter Spicy

Flavor Strength:

Too Weak   Just Right   Too Strong

Notes: Date: ___/___/___

Caffeine: Y N

SODA CHARACTERISTICS	SCORE
Bottle Shape, Style, & Color	
Labeling Aesthetics & Description	
Aroma & Drink Color	
Carbonation / Fizziness	
Drinkability / Refreshment	
Tastes as Advertised & Expected	
Overall Flavor	
Aftertaste / Finish	
Memorability	
Value for Price	
BOTTLECAP SCORE	

Brand: _____

Flavor: _____

Flavor Type:

Sweet   Tart/Sour   Herbal   Bitter   Spicy

Flavor Strength:

Too Weak   Just Right   Too Strong

Notes: Date: ___/___/___

Caffeine: Y N

SODA CHARACTERISTICS	SCORE
Bottle Shape, Style, & Color	
Labeling Aesthetics & Description	
Aroma & Drink Color	
Carbonation / Fizziness	
Drinkability / Refreshment	
Tastes as Advertised & Expected	
Overall Flavor	
Aftertaste / Finish	
Memorability	
Value for Price	
BOTTLECAP SCORE	

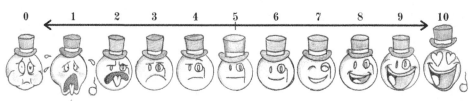

0 1 2 3 4 5 6 7 8 9 10

Brand: _____

Flavor: _____

Flavor Type:

Sweet   Tart/Sour   Herbal   Bitter   Spicy

Flavor Strength:

Too Weak   Just Right   Too Strong

Notes: Date: ___/___/___

Caffeine: Y N

SODA CHARACTERISTICS	SCORE
Bottle Shape, Style, & Color	
Labeling Aesthetics & Description	
Aroma & Drink Color	
Carbonation / Fizziness	
Drinkability / Refreshment	
Tastes as Advertised & Expected	
Overall Flavor	
Aftertaste / Finish	
Memorability	
Value for Price	
BOTTLECAP SCORE	

COLA FLAVORS

Brand: _____
Flavor: _____

Flavor Type:

Sweet   Tart/Sour   Herbal   Bitter   Spicy

Flavor Strength:

Too Weak   Just Right   Too Strong

Notes: Date: ___/___/___
              Caffeine: Y   N

SODA CHARACTERISTICS	SCORE
Bottle Shape, Style, & Color	
Labeling Aesthetics & Description	
Aroma & Drink Color	
Carbonation / Fizziness	
Drinkability / Refreshment	
Tastes as Advertised & Expected	
Overall Flavor	
Aftertaste / Finish	
Memorability	
Value for Price	
BOTTLECAP SCORE	

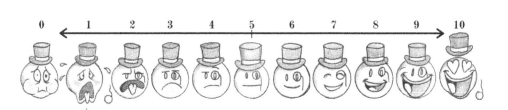

Brand: _____
Flavor: _____

Flavor Type:

Sweet   Tart/Sour   Herbal   Bitter   Spicy

Flavor Strength:

Too Weak   Just Right   Too Strong

Notes: Date: ___/___/___
              Caffeine: Y   N

SODA CHARACTERISTICS	SCORE
Bottle Shape, Style, & Color	
Labeling Aesthetics & Description	
Aroma & Drink Color	
Carbonation / Fizziness	
Drinkability / Refreshment	
Tastes as Advertised & Expected	
Overall Flavor	
Aftertaste / Finish	
Memorability	
Value for Price	
BOTTLECAP SCORE	

Brand: _____

Flavor: _____

Flavor Type:

Sweet   Tart/Sour   Herbal   Bitter   Spicy

Flavor Strength:

Too Weak   Just Right   Too Strong

Notes: Date: ___/___/___

Caffeine: Y N

SODA CHARACTERISTICS	SCORE
Bottle Shape, Style, & Color	
Labeling Aesthetics & Description	
Aroma & Drink Color	
Carbonation / Fizziness	
Drinkability / Refreshment	
Tastes as Advertised & Expected	
Overall Flavor	
Aftertaste / Finish	
Memorability	
Value for Price	
BOTTLECAP SCORE	

Brand: _____

Flavor: _____

Flavor Type:

Sweet   Tart/Sour   Herbal   Bitter   Spicy

Flavor Strength:

Too Weak   Just Right   Too Strong

Notes: Date: ___/___/___

Caffeine: Y N

SODA CHARACTERISTICS	SCORE
Bottle Shape, Style, & Color	
Labeling Aesthetics & Description	
Aroma & Drink Color	
Carbonation / Fizziness	
Drinkability / Refreshment	
Tastes as Advertised & Expected	
Overall Flavor	
Aftertaste / Finish	
Memorability	
Value for Price	
BOTTLECAP SCORE	

Brand: _____

Flavor: _____

Flavor Type:				
Sweet	Tart/Sour	Herbal	Bitter	Spicy

Flavor Strength:

Too Weak   Just Right   Too Strong

Notes: Date: ___/___/___

Caffeine: Y N

SODA CHARACTERISTICS	SCORE
Bottle Shape, Style, & Color	
Labeling Aesthetics & Description	
Aroma & Drink Color	
Carbonation / Fizziness	
Drinkability / Refreshment	
Tastes as Advertised & Expected	
Overall Flavor	
Aftertaste / Finish	
Memorability	
Value for Price	
BOTTLECAP SCORE	

0   1   2   3   4   5   6   7   8   9   10

Brand: _____

Flavor: _____

Flavor Type:				
Sweet	Tart/Sour	Herbal	Bitter	Spicy

Flavor Strength:

Too Weak   Just Right   Too Strong

Notes: Date: ___/___/___

Caffeine: Y N

SODA CHARACTERISTICS	SCORE
Bottle Shape, Style, & Color	
Labeling Aesthetics & Description	
Aroma & Drink Color	
Carbonation / Fizziness	
Drinkability / Refreshment	
Tastes as Advertised & Expected	
Overall Flavor	
Aftertaste / Finish	
Memorability	
Value for Price	
BOTTLECAP SCORE	

Brand: _____

Flavor: _____

Flavor Type:

Sweet   Tart/Sour   Herbal   Bitter   Spicy

Flavor Strength:

|——————————|——————————|——————————|
Too Weak   Just Right   Too Strong

Notes: Date: ___/___/___

                 Caffeine: Y   N

SODA CHARACTERISTICS	SCORE
Bottle Shape, Style, & Color	
Labeling Aesthetics & Description	
Aroma & Drink Color	
Carbonation / Fizziness	
Drinkability / Refreshment	
Tastes as Advertised & Expected	
Overall Flavor	
Aftertaste / Finish	
Memorability	
Value for Price	
BOTTLECAP SCORE	

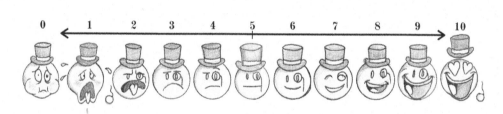

0   1   2   3   4   5   6   7   8   9   10

Brand: _____

Flavor: _____

Flavor Type:

Sweet   Tart/Sour   Herbal   Bitter   Spicy

Flavor Strength:

|——————————|——————————|——————————|
Too Weak   Just Right   Too Strong

Notes: Date: ___/___/___

                 Caffeine: Y   N

SODA CHARACTERISTICS	SCORE
Bottle Shape, Style, & Color	
Labeling Aesthetics & Description	
Aroma & Drink Color	
Carbonation / Fizziness	
Drinkability / Refreshment	
Tastes as Advertised & Expected	
Overall Flavor	
Aftertaste / Finish	
Memorability	
Value for Price	
BOTTLECAP SCORE	

COLA FLAVORS

Brand: _____

Flavor: _____

Flavor Type:

Sweet   Tart/Sour   Herbal   Bitter   Spicy

Flavor Strength:

Too Weak   Just Right   Too Strong

Notes: Date: ___/___/___

Caffeine: Y N

SODA CHARACTERISTICS	SCORE
Bottle Shape, Style, & Color	
Labeling Aesthetics & Description	
Aroma & Drink Color	
Carbonation / Fizziness	
Drinkability / Refreshment	
Tastes as Advertised & Expected	
Overall Flavor	
Aftertaste / Finish	
Memorability	
Value for Price	
BOTTLECAP SCORE	

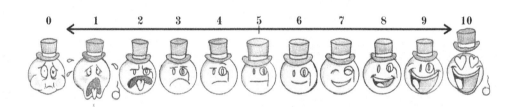

0   1   2   3   4   5   6   7   8   9   10

Brand: _____

Flavor: _____

Flavor Type:

Sweet   Tart/Sour   Herbal   Bitter   Spicy

Flavor Strength:

Too Weak   Just Right   Too Strong

Notes: Date: ___/___/___

Caffeine: Y N

SODA CHARACTERISTICS	SCORE
Bottle Shape, Style, & Color	
Labeling Aesthetics & Description	
Aroma & Drink Color	
Carbonation / Fizziness	
Drinkability / Refreshment	
Tastes as Advertised & Expected	
Overall Flavor	
Aftertaste / Finish	
Memorability	
Value for Price	
BOTTLECAP SCORE	

Brand: _____

Flavor: _____

Flavor Type:

Sweet   Tart/Sour   Herbal   Bitter   Spicy

Flavor Strength:

Too Weak   Just Right   Too Strong

Notes: Date: ___/___/___

Caffeine: Y N

SODA CHARACTERISTICS	SCORE
Bottle Shape, Style, & Color	
Labeling Aesthetics & Description	
Aroma & Drink Color	
Carbonation / Fizziness	
Drinkability / Refreshment	
Tastes as Advertised & Expected	
Overall Flavor	
Aftertaste / Finish	
Memorability	
Value for Price	
BOTTLECAP SCORE	

0   1   2   3   4   5   6   7   8   9   10

Brand: _____

Flavor: _____

Flavor Type:

Sweet   Tart/Sour   Herbal   Bitter   Spicy

Flavor Strength:

Too Weak   Just Right   Too Strong

Notes: Date: ___/___/___

Caffeine: Y N

SODA CHARACTERISTICS	SCORE
Bottle Shape, Style, & Color	
Labeling Aesthetics & Description	
Aroma & Drink Color	
Carbonation / Fizziness	
Drinkability / Refreshment	
Tastes as Advertised & Expected	
Overall Flavor	
Aftertaste / Finish	
Memorability	
Value for Price	
BOTTLECAP SCORE	

COLA FLAVORS

Brand: _____

Flavor: _____

Flavor Type:

Sweet   Tart/Sour   Herbal   Bitter   Spicy

Flavor Strength:

Too Weak   Just Right   Too Strong

Notes: Date: ___/___/___

Caffeine: Y N

SODA CHARACTERISTICS	SCORE
Bottle Shape, Style, & Color	
Labeling Aesthetics & Description	
Aroma & Drink Color	
Carbonation / Fizziness	
Drinkability / Refreshment	
Tastes as Advertised & Expected	
Overall Flavor	
Aftertaste / Finish	
Memorability	
Value for Price	
BOTTLECAP SCORE	

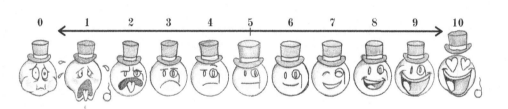

0 1 2 3 4 5 6 7 8 9 10

Brand: _____

Flavor: _____

Flavor Type:

Sweet   Tart/Sour   Herbal   Bitter   Spicy

Flavor Strength:

Too Weak   Just Right   Too Strong

Notes: Date: ___/___/___

Caffeine: Y N

SODA CHARACTERISTICS	SCORE
Bottle Shape, Style, & Color	
Labeling Aesthetics & Description	
Aroma & Drink Color	
Carbonation / Fizziness	
Drinkability / Refreshment	
Tastes as Advertised & Expected	
Overall Flavor	
Aftertaste / Finish	
Memorability	
Value for Price	
BOTTLECAP SCORE	

77

Brand: _____

Flavor: _____

Flavor Type:				
Sweet	Tart/Sour	Herbal	Bitter	Spicy

Flavor Strength:

Too Weak   Just Right   Too Strong

Notes: Date: ___/___/___

Caffeine: Y N

SODA CHARACTERISTICS	SCORE
Bottle Shape, Style, & Color	
Labeling Aesthetics & Description	
Aroma & Drink Color	
Carbonation / Fizziness	
Drinkability / Refreshment	
Tastes as Advertised & Expected	
Overall Flavor	
Aftertaste / Finish	
Memorability	
Value for Price	
BOTTLECAP SCORE	

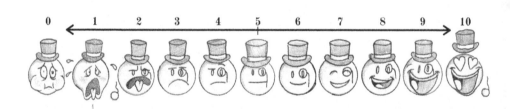

0   1   2   3   4   5   6   7   8   9   10

Brand: _____

Flavor: _____

Flavor Type:				
Sweet	Tart/Sour	Herbal	Bitter	Spicy

Flavor Strength:

Too Weak   Just Right   Too Strong

Notes: Date: ___/___/___

Caffeine: Y N

SODA CHARACTERISTICS	SCORE
Bottle Shape, Style, & Color	
Labeling Aesthetics & Description	
Aroma & Drink Color	
Carbonation / Fizziness	
Drinkability / Refreshment	
Tastes as Advertised & Expected	
Overall Flavor	
Aftertaste / Finish	
Memorability	
Value for Price	
BOTTLECAP SCORE	

Brand: _____

Flavor: _____

Flavor Type:

Sweet   Tart/Sour   Herbal   Bitter   Spicy

Flavor Strength:

Too Weak   Just Right   Too Strong

Notes: Date: ___/___/___

Caffeine: Y N

SODA CHARACTERISTICS	SCORE
Bottle Shape, Style, & Color	
Labeling Aesthetics & Description	
Aroma & Drink Color	
Carbonation / Fizziness	
Drinkability / Refreshment	
Tastes as Advertised & Expected	
Overall Flavor	
Aftertaste / Finish	
Memorability	
Value for Price	
BOTTLECAP SCORE	

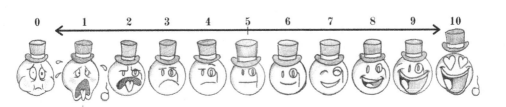

0   1   2   3   4   5   6   7   8   9   10

Brand: _____

Flavor: _____

Flavor Type:

Sweet   Tart/Sour   Herbal   Bitter   Spicy

Flavor Strength:

Too Weak   Just Right   Too Strong

Notes: Date: ___/___/___

Caffeine: Y N

SODA CHARACTERISTICS	SCORE
Bottle Shape, Style, & Color	
Labeling Aesthetics & Description	
Aroma & Drink Color	
Carbonation / Fizziness	
Drinkability / Refreshment	
Tastes as Advertised & Expected	
Overall Flavor	
Aftertaste / Finish	
Memorability	
Value for Price	
BOTTLECAP SCORE	

COLA FLAVORS

Brand: _____

Flavor: _____

Flavor Type:

Sweet   Tart/Sour   Herbal   Bitter   Spicy

Flavor Strength:

Too Weak   Just Right   Too Strong

Notes: Date: ___/___/___

Caffeine: Y   N

SODA CHARACTERISTICS	SCORE
Bottle Shape, Style, & Color	
Labeling Aesthetics & Description	
Aroma & Drink Color	
Carbonation / Fizziness	
Drinkability / Refreshment	
Tastes as Advertised & Expected	
Overall Flavor	
Aftertaste / Finish	
Memorability	
Value for Price	
BOTTLECAP SCORE	

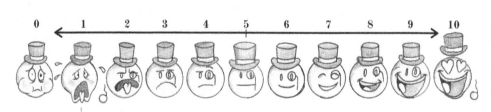

Brand: _____

Flavor: _____

Flavor Type:

Sweet   Tart/Sour   Herbal   Bitter   Spicy

Flavor Strength:

Too Weak   Just Right   Too Strong

Notes: Date: ___/___/___

Caffeine: Y   N

SODA CHARACTERISTICS	SCORE
Bottle Shape, Style, & Color	
Labeling Aesthetics & Description	
Aroma & Drink Color	
Carbonation / Fizziness	
Drinkability / Refreshment	
Tastes as Advertised & Expected	
Overall Flavor	
Aftertaste / Finish	
Memorability	
Value for Price	
BOTTLECAP SCORE	

COLA FLAVORS

Brand: _____

Flavor: _____

Flavor Type:

Sweet   Tart/Sour   Herbal   Bitter   Spicy

Flavor Strength:

Too Weak   Just Right   Too Strong

Notes: Date: ___/___/___

Caffeine: Y   N

SODA CHARACTERISTICS	SCORE
Bottle Shape, Style, & Color	
Labeling Aesthetics & Description	
Aroma & Drink Color	
Carbonation / Fizziness	
Drinkability / Refreshment	
Tastes as Advertised & Expected	
Overall Flavor	
Aftertaste / Finish	
Memorability	
Value for Price	
BOTTLECAP SCORE	

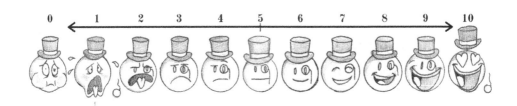

0   1   2   3   4   5   6   7   8   9   10

Brand: _____

Flavor: _____

Flavor Type:

Sweet   Tart/Sour   Herbal   Bitter   Spicy

Flavor Strength:

Too Weak   Just Right   Too Strong

Notes: Date: ___/___/___

Caffeine: Y   N

SODA CHARACTERISTICS	SCORE
Bottle Shape, Style, & Color	
Labeling Aesthetics & Description	
Aroma & Drink Color	
Carbonation / Fizziness	
Drinkability / Refreshment	
Tastes as Advertised & Expected	
Overall Flavor	
Aftertaste / Finish	
Memorability	
Value for Price	
BOTTLECAP SCORE	

CREAM SODA FLAVORS

Brand	Flavor	Score	Notes	Page
				83
				83
				84
				84
				85
				85
				86
				86
				87
				87
				88
				88
				89
				89
				90
				90
				91
				91
				92
				92
				93
				93
				94
				94
				95
				95

Brand: _____

Flavor: _____

SODA CHARACTERISTICS	SCORE
Bottle Shape, Style, & Color	
Labeling Aesthetics & Description	
Aroma & Drink Color	
Carbonation / Fizziness	
Drinkability / Refreshment	
Tastes as Advertised & Expected	
Overall Flavor	
Aftertaste / Finish	
Memorability	
Value for Price	
BOTTLECAP SCORE	

Flavor Type:

Sweet   Tart/Sour   Herbal   Bitter   Spicy

Flavor Strength:

Too Weak   Just Right   Too Strong

Notes: Date: ___/___/___

Caffeine: Y N

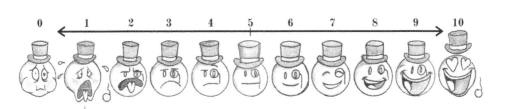

0   1   2   3   4   5   6   7   8   9   10

Brand: _____

Flavor: _____

SODA CHARACTERISTICS	SCORE
Bottle Shape, Style, & Color	
Labeling Aesthetics & Description	
Aroma & Drink Color	
Carbonation / Fizziness	
Drinkability / Refreshment	
Tastes as Advertised & Expected	
Overall Flavor	
Aftertaste / Finish	
Memorability	
Value for Price	
BOTTLECAP SCORE	

Flavor Type:

Sweet   Tart/Sour   Herbal   Bitter   Spicy

Flavor Strength:

Too Weak   Just Right   Too Strong

Notes: Date: ___/___/___

Caffeine: Y N

Brand: _____

Flavor: _____

Flavor Type:

Sweet   Tart/Sour   Herbal   Bitter   Spicy

Flavor Strength:

Too Weak   Just Right   Too Strong

Notes: Date: ___/___/___

                    Caffeine: Y N

SODA CHARACTERISTICS	SCORE
Bottle Shape, Style, & Color	
Labeling Aesthetics & Description	
Aroma & Drink Color	
Carbonation / Fizziness	
Drinkability / Refreshment	
Tastes as Advertised & Expected	
Overall Flavor	
Aftertaste / Finish	
Memorability	
Value for Price	
BOTTLECAP SCORE	

Brand: _____

Flavor: _____

Flavor Type:

Sweet   Tart/Sour   Herbal   Bitter   Spicy

Flavor Strength:

Too Weak   Just Right   Too Strong

Notes: Date: ___/___/___

                    Caffeine: Y N

SODA CHARACTERISTICS	SCORE
Bottle Shape, Style, & Color	
Labeling Aesthetics & Description	
Aroma & Drink Color	
Carbonation / Fizziness	
Drinkability / Refreshment	
Tastes as Advertised & Expected	
Overall Flavor	
Aftertaste / Finish	
Memorability	
Value for Price	
BOTTLECAP SCORE	

Brand: _____

Flavor: _____

SODA CHARACTERISTICS	**SCORE**
Bottle Shape, Style, & Color	
Labeling Aesthetics & Description	
Aroma & Drink Color	
Carbonation / Fizziness	
Drinkability / Refreshment	
Tastes as Advertised & Expected	
Overall Flavor	
Aftertaste / Finish	
Memorability	
Value for Price	
BOTTLECAP SCORE	

Flavor Type:

Sweet   Tart/Sour   Herbal   Bitter   Spicy

Flavor Strength:

Too Weak   Just Right   Too Strong

Notes: Date: ___/___/___

Caffeine: Y   N

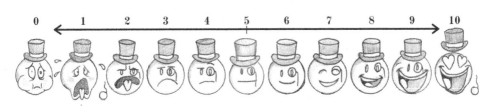

Brand: _____

Flavor: _____

SODA CHARACTERISTICS	**SCORE**
Bottle Shape, Style, & Color	
Labeling Aesthetics & Description	
Aroma & Drink Color	
Carbonation / Fizziness	
Drinkability / Refreshment	
Tastes as Advertised & Expected	
Overall Flavor	
Aftertaste / Finish	
Memorability	
Value for Price	
BOTTLECAP SCORE	

Flavor Type:

Sweet   Tart/Sour   Herbal   Bitter   Spicy

Flavor Strength:

Too Weak   Just Right   Too Strong

Notes: Date: ___/___/___

Caffeine: Y   N

Brand: _____

Flavor: _____

Flavor Type:

Sweet   Tart/Sour   Herbal   Bitter   Spicy

Flavor Strength:

Too Weak   Just Right   Too Strong

Notes: Date: ___/___/___

Caffeine: Y N

SODA CHARACTERISTICS	SCORE
Bottle Shape, Style, & Color	
Labeling Aesthetics & Description	
Aroma & Drink Color	
Carbonation / Fizziness	
Drinkability / Refreshment	
Tastes as Advertised & Expected	
Overall Flavor	
Aftertaste / Finish	
Memorability	
Value for Price	
BOTTLECAP SCORE	

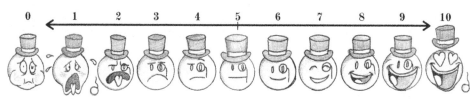

Brand: _____

Flavor: _____

Flavor Type:

Sweet   Tart/Sour   Herbal   Bitter   Spicy

Flavor Strength:

Too Weak   Just Right   Too Strong

Notes: Date: ___/___/___

Caffeine: Y N

SODA CHARACTERISTICS	SCORE
Bottle Shape, Style, & Color	
Labeling Aesthetics & Description	
Aroma & Drink Color	
Carbonation / Fizziness	
Drinkability / Refreshment	
Tastes as Advertised & Expected	
Overall Flavor	
Aftertaste / Finish	
Memorability	
Value for Price	
BOTTLECAP SCORE	

Brand: _____

Flavor: _____

Flavor Type:

Sweet   Tart/Sour   Herbal   Bitter   Spicy

Flavor Strength:

Too Weak   Just Right   Too Strong

Notes: Date: ___/___/___

Caffeine: Y N

SODA CHARACTERISTICS	SCORE
Bottle Shape, Style, & Color	
Labeling Aesthetics & Description	
Aroma & Drink Color	
Carbonation / Fizziness	
Drinkability / Refreshment	
Tastes as Advertised & Expected	
Overall Flavor	
Aftertaste / Finish	
Memorability	
Value for Price	
BOTTLECAP SCORE	

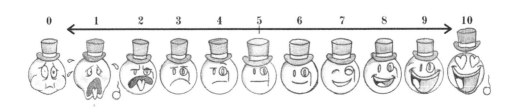

Brand: _____

Flavor: _____

Flavor Type:

Sweet   Tart/Sour   Herbal   Bitter   Spicy

Flavor Strength:

Too Weak   Just Right   Too Strong

Notes: Date: ___/___/___

Caffeine: Y N

SODA CHARACTERISTICS	SCORE
Bottle Shape, Style, & Color	
Labeling Aesthetics & Description	
Aroma & Drink Color	
Carbonation / Fizziness	
Drinkability / Refreshment	
Tastes as Advertised & Expected	
Overall Flavor	
Aftertaste / Finish	
Memorability	
Value for Price	
BOTTLECAP SCORE	

Brand: _____

Flavor: _____

Flavor Type:

Sweet   Tart/Sour   Herbal   Bitter   Spicy

Flavor Strength:

Too Weak   Just Right   Too Strong

Notes: Date: ___/___/___

Caffeine: Y N

SODA CHARACTERISTICS	SCORE
Bottle Shape, Style, & Color	
Labeling Aesthetics & Description	
Aroma & Drink Color	
Carbonation / Fizziness	
Drinkability / Refreshment	
Tastes as Advertised & Expected	
Overall Flavor	
Aftertaste / Finish	
Memorability	
Value for Price	
BOTTLECAP SCORE	

0   1   2   3   4   5   6   7   8   9   10

Brand: _____

Flavor: _____

Flavor Type:

Sweet   Tart/Sour   Herbal   Bitter   Spicy

Flavor Strength:

Too Weak   Just Right   Too Strong

Notes: Date: ___/___/___

Caffeine: Y N

SODA CHARACTERISTICS	SCORE
Bottle Shape, Style, & Color	
Labeling Aesthetics & Description	
Aroma & Drink Color	
Carbonation / Fizziness	
Drinkability / Refreshment	
Tastes as Advertised & Expected	
Overall Flavor	
Aftertaste / Finish	
Memorability	
Value for Price	
BOTTLECAP SCORE	

Brand: _____

Flavor: _____

Flavor Type:

Sweet   Tart/Sour   Herbal   Bitter   Spicy

Flavor Strength:

Too Weak   Just Right   Too Strong

Notes: Date: ___/___/___

              Caffeine: Y N

SODA CHARACTERISTICS	SCORE
Bottle Shape, Style, & Color	
Labeling Aesthetics & Description	
Aroma & Drink Color	
Carbonation / Fizziness	
Drinkability / Refreshment	
Tastes as Advertised & Expected	
Overall Flavor	
Aftertaste / Finish	
Memorability	
Value for Price	
BOTTLECAP SCORE	

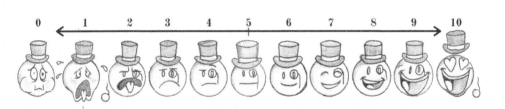

| 0 | 1 | 2 | 3 | 4 | 5 | 6 | 7 | 8 | 9 | 10 |

Brand: _____

Flavor: _____

Flavor Type:

Sweet   Tart/Sour   Herbal   Bitter   Spicy

Flavor Strength:

Too Weak   Just Right   Too Strong

Notes: Date: ___/___/___

              Caffeine: Y N

SODA CHARACTERISTICS	SCORE
Bottle Shape, Style, & Color	
Labeling Aesthetics & Description	
Aroma & Drink Color	
Carbonation / Fizziness	
Drinkability / Refreshment	
Tastes as Advertised & Expected	
Overall Flavor	
Aftertaste / Finish	
Memorability	
Value for Price	
BOTTLECAP SCORE	

Brand: _____

Flavor: _____

SODA CHARACTERISTICS	SCORE
Bottle Shape, Style, & Color	
Labeling Aesthetics & Description	
Aroma & Drink Color	
Carbonation / Fizziness	
Drinkability / Refreshment	
Tastes as Advertised & Expected	
Overall Flavor	
Aftertaste / Finish	
Memorability	
Value for Price	
BOTTLECAP SCORE	

Flavor Type:

Sweet   Tart/Sour   Herbal   Bitter   Spicy

Flavor Strength:

Too Weak   Just Right   Too Strong

Notes: Date: ___/___/___

          Caffeine: Y N

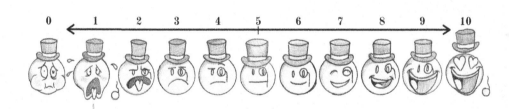

Brand: _____

Flavor: _____

SODA CHARACTERISTICS	SCORE
Bottle Shape, Style, & Color	
Labeling Aesthetics & Description	
Aroma & Drink Color	
Carbonation / Fizziness	
Drinkability / Refreshment	
Tastes as Advertised & Expected	
Overall Flavor	
Aftertaste / Finish	
Memorability	
Value for Price	
BOTTLECAP SCORE	

Flavor Type:

Sweet   Tart/Sour   Herbal   Bitter   Spicy

Flavor Strength:

Too Weak   Just Right   Too Strong

Notes: Date: ___/___/___

          Caffeine: Y N

Brand: _____

Flavor: _____

Flavor Type:				
Sweet	Tart/Sour	Herbal	Bitter	Spicy

Flavor Strength:

Too Weak   Just Right   Too Strong

Notes: Date: ___/___/___

Caffeine: Y N

SODA CHARACTERISTICS	SCORE
Bottle Shape, Style, & Color	
Labeling Aesthetics & Description	
Aroma & Drink Color	
Carbonation / Fizziness	
Drinkability / Refreshment	
Tastes as Advertised & Expected	
Overall Flavor	
Aftertaste / Finish	
Memorability	
Value for Price	
BOTTLECAP SCORE	

0   1   2   3   4   5   6   7   8   9   10

Brand: _____

Flavor: _____

Flavor Type:				
Sweet	Tart/Sour	Herbal	Bitter	Spicy

Flavor Strength:

Too Weak   Just Right   Too Strong

Notes: Date: ___/___/___

Caffeine: Y N

SODA CHARACTERISTICS	SCORE
Bottle Shape, Style, & Color	
Labeling Aesthetics & Description	
Aroma & Drink Color	
Carbonation / Fizziness	
Drinkability / Refreshment	
Tastes as Advertised & Expected	
Overall Flavor	
Aftertaste / Finish	
Memorability	
Value for Price	
BOTTLECAP SCORE	

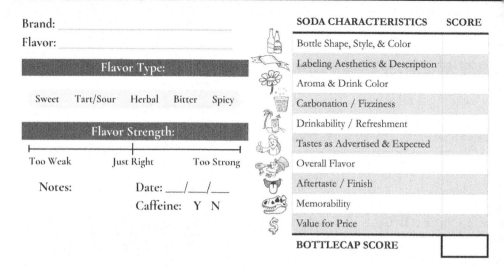

Brand: _____

Flavor: _____

Flavor Type:				
Sweet	Tart/Sour	Herbal	Bitter	Spicy

Flavor Strength:

Too Weak — Just Right — Too Strong

Notes:

Date: ___/___/___

Caffeine: Y N

SODA CHARACTERISTICS	SCORE
Bottle Shape, Style, & Color	
Labeling Aesthetics & Description	
Aroma & Drink Color	
Carbonation / Fizziness	
Drinkability / Refreshment	
Tastes as Advertised & Expected	
Overall Flavor	
Aftertaste / Finish	
Memorability	
Value for Price	
BOTTLECAP SCORE	

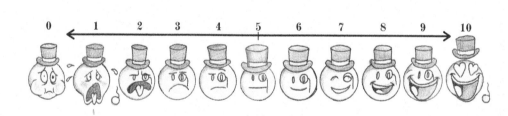

0 1 2 3 4 5 6 7 8 9 10

Brand: _____

Flavor: _____

Flavor Type:				
Sweet	Tart/Sour	Herbal	Bitter	Spicy

Flavor Strength:

Too Weak — Just Right — Too Strong

Notes:

Date: ___/___/___

Caffeine: Y N

SODA CHARACTERISTICS	SCORE
Bottle Shape, Style, & Color	
Labeling Aesthetics & Description	
Aroma & Drink Color	
Carbonation / Fizziness	
Drinkability / Refreshment	
Tastes as Advertised & Expected	
Overall Flavor	
Aftertaste / Finish	
Memorability	
Value for Price	
BOTTLECAP SCORE	

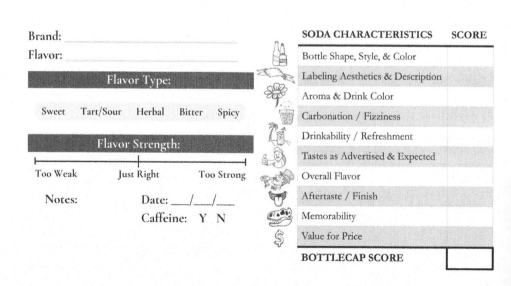

Brand: _____

Flavor: _____

Flavor Type:

Sweet   Tart/Sour   Herbal   Bitter   Spicy

Flavor Strength:

Too Weak   Just Right   Too Strong

Notes: Date: ___/___/___

Caffeine: Y N

SODA CHARACTERISTICS	SCORE
Bottle Shape, Style, & Color	
Labeling Aesthetics & Description	
Aroma & Drink Color	
Carbonation / Fizziness	
Drinkability / Refreshment	
Tastes as Advertised & Expected	
Overall Flavor	
Aftertaste / Finish	
Memorability	
Value for Price	
BOTTLECAP SCORE	

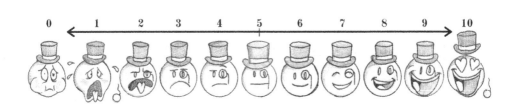

Brand: _____

Flavor: _____

Flavor Type:

Sweet   Tart/Sour   Herbal   Bitter   Spicy

Flavor Strength:

Too Weak   Just Right   Too Strong

Notes: Date: ___/___/___

Caffeine: Y N

SODA CHARACTERISTICS	SCORE
Bottle Shape, Style, & Color	
Labeling Aesthetics & Description	
Aroma & Drink Color	
Carbonation / Fizziness	
Drinkability / Refreshment	
Tastes as Advertised & Expected	
Overall Flavor	
Aftertaste / Finish	
Memorability	
Value for Price	
BOTTLECAP SCORE	

Brand: _____

Flavor: _____

Flavor Type:

Sweet   Tart/Sour   Herbal   Bitter   Spicy

Flavor Strength:

Too Weak   Just Right   Too Strong

Notes: Date: ___/___/___

Caffeine: Y N

SODA CHARACTERISTICS	SCORE
Bottle Shape, Style, & Color	
Labeling Aesthetics & Description	
Aroma & Drink Color	
Carbonation / Fizziness	
Drinkability / Refreshment	
Tastes as Advertised & Expected	
Overall Flavor	
Aftertaste / Finish	
Memorability	
Value for Price	
BOTTLECAP SCORE	

Brand: _____

Flavor: _____

Flavor Type:

Sweet   Tart/Sour   Herbal   Bitter   Spicy

Flavor Strength:

Too Weak   Just Right   Too Strong

Notes: Date: ___/___/___

Caffeine: Y N

SODA CHARACTERISTICS	SCORE
Bottle Shape, Style, & Color	
Labeling Aesthetics & Description	
Aroma & Drink Color	
Carbonation / Fizziness	
Drinkability / Refreshment	
Tastes as Advertised & Expected	
Overall Flavor	
Aftertaste / Finish	
Memorability	
Value for Price	
BOTTLECAP SCORE	

Brand: _____

Flavor: _____

Flavor Type:				
Sweet	Tart/Sour	Herbal	Bitter	Spicy

Flavor Strength:

Too Weak — Just Right — Too Strong

Notes: Date: ___/___/___

Caffeine: Y N

SODA CHARACTERISTICS	SCORE
Bottle Shape, Style, & Color	
Labeling Aesthetics & Description	
Aroma & Drink Color	
Carbonation / Fizziness	
Drinkability / Refreshment	
Tastes as Advertised & Expected	
Overall Flavor	
Aftertaste / Finish	
Memorability	
Value for Price	
BOTTLECAP SCORE	

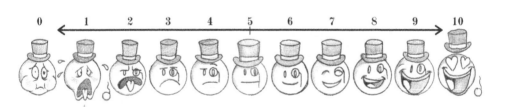

0   1   2   3   4   5   6   7   8   9   10

Brand: _____

Flavor: _____

Flavor Type:				
Sweet	Tart/Sour	Herbal	Bitter	Spicy

Flavor Strength:

Too Weak — Just Right — Too Strong

Notes: Date: ___/___/___

Caffeine: Y N

SODA CHARACTERISTICS	SCORE
Bottle Shape, Style, & Color	
Labeling Aesthetics & Description	
Aroma & Drink Color	
Carbonation / Fizziness	
Drinkability / Refreshment	
Tastes as Advertised & Expected	
Overall Flavor	
Aftertaste / Finish	
Memorability	
Value for Price	
BOTTLECAP SCORE	

DESERT FLAVORS

Brand	Flavor	Score	Notes	Page
				97
				97
				98
				98
				99
				99
				100
				100
				101
				101
				102
				102
				103
				103
				104
				104
				105
				105
				106
				106
				107
				107
				108
				108
				109
				109

Brand: _____

Flavor: _____

Flavor Type:

Sweet   Tart/Sour   Herbal   Bitter   Spicy

Flavor Strength:

Too Weak   Just Right   Too Strong

Notes: Date: ___/___/___

      Caffeine: Y   N

SODA CHARACTERISTICS	SCORE
Bottle Shape, Style, & Color	
Labeling Aesthetics & Description	
Aroma & Drink Color	
Carbonation / Fizziness	
Drinkability / Refreshment	
Tastes as Advertised & Expected	
Overall Flavor	
Aftertaste / Finish	
Memorability	
Value for Price	
BOTTLECAP SCORE	

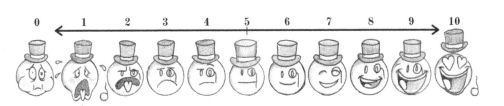

0   1   2   3   4   5   6   7   8   9   10

Brand: _____

Flavor: _____

Flavor Type:

Sweet   Tart/Sour   Herbal   Bitter   Spicy

Flavor Strength:

Too Weak   Just Right   Too Strong

Notes: Date: ___/___/___

      Caffeine: Y   N

SODA CHARACTERISTICS	SCORE
Bottle Shape, Style, & Color	
Labeling Aesthetics & Description	
Aroma & Drink Color	
Carbonation / Fizziness	
Drinkability / Refreshment	
Tastes as Advertised & Expected	
Overall Flavor	
Aftertaste / Finish	
Memorability	
Value for Price	
BOTTLECAP SCORE	

Brand: _____

Flavor: _____

Flavor Type:

Sweet   Tart/Sour   Herbal   Bitter   Spicy

Flavor Strength:

Too Weak   Just Right   Too Strong

Notes: Date: __/__/__

                Caffeine: Y N

SODA CHARACTERISTICS	SCORE
Bottle Shape, Style, & Color	
Labeling Aesthetics & Description	
Aroma & Drink Color	
Carbonation / Fizziness	
Drinkability / Refreshment	
Tastes as Advertised & Expected	
Overall Flavor	
Aftertaste / Finish	
Memorability	
Value for Price	
BOTTLECAP SCORE	

0   1   2   3   4   5   6   7   8   9   10

Brand: _____

Flavor: _____

Flavor Type:

Sweet   Tart/Sour   Herbal   Bitter   Spicy

Flavor Strength:

Too Weak   Just Right   Too Strong

Notes: Date: __/__/__

                Caffeine: Y N

SODA CHARACTERISTICS	SCORE
Bottle Shape, Style, & Color	
Labeling Aesthetics & Description	
Aroma & Drink Color	
Carbonation / Fizziness	
Drinkability / Refreshment	
Tastes as Advertised & Expected	
Overall Flavor	
Aftertaste / Finish	
Memorability	
Value for Price	
BOTTLECAP SCORE	

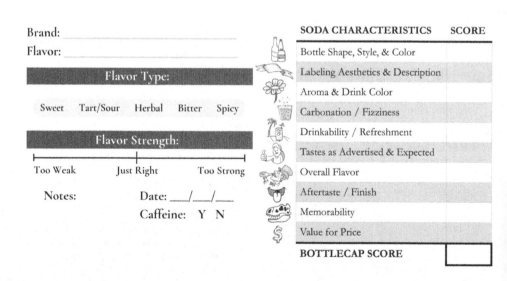

Brand: _____

Flavor: _____

Flavor Type:				
Sweet	Tart/Sour	Herbal	Bitter	Spicy

Flavor Strength:

Too Weak   Just Right   Too Strong

Notes: Date: ___/___/___

          Caffeine: Y N

SODA CHARACTERISTICS	SCORE
Bottle Shape, Style, & Color	
Labeling Aesthetics & Description	
Aroma & Drink Color	
Carbonation / Fizziness	
Drinkability / Refreshment	
Tastes as Advertised & Expected	
Overall Flavor	
Aftertaste / Finish	
Memorability	
Value for Price	
BOTTLECAP SCORE	

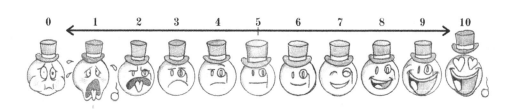

Brand: _____

Flavor: _____

Flavor Type:				
Sweet	Tart/Sour	Herbal	Bitter	Spicy

Flavor Strength:

Too Weak   Just Right   Too Strong

Notes: Date: ___/___/___

          Caffeine: Y N

SODA CHARACTERISTICS	SCORE
Bottle Shape, Style, & Color	
Labeling Aesthetics & Description	
Aroma & Drink Color	
Carbonation / Fizziness	
Drinkability / Refreshment	
Tastes as Advertised & Expected	
Overall Flavor	
Aftertaste / Finish	
Memorability	
Value for Price	
BOTTLECAP SCORE	

Brand: _____

Flavor: _____

Flavor Type:

Sweet   Tart/Sour   Herbal   Bitter   Spicy

Flavor Strength:

Too Weak   Just Right   Too Strong

Notes: Date: ___/___/___

Caffeine: Y N

SODA CHARACTERISTICS	SCORE
Bottle Shape, Style, & Color	
Labeling Aesthetics & Description	
Aroma & Drink Color	
Carbonation / Fizziness	
Drinkability / Refreshment	
Tastes as Advertised & Expected	
Overall Flavor	
Aftertaste / Finish	
Memorability	
Value for Price	
BOTTLECAP SCORE	

0   1   2   3   4   5   6   7   8   9   10

Brand: _____

Flavor: _____

Flavor Type:

Sweet   Tart/Sour   Herbal   Bitter   Spicy

Flavor Strength:

Too Weak   Just Right   Too Strong

Notes: Date: ___/___/___

Caffeine: Y N

SODA CHARACTERISTICS	SCORE
Bottle Shape, Style, & Color	
Labeling Aesthetics & Description	
Aroma & Drink Color	
Carbonation / Fizziness	
Drinkability / Refreshment	
Tastes as Advertised & Expected	
Overall Flavor	
Aftertaste / Finish	
Memorability	
Value for Price	
BOTTLECAP SCORE	

Brand: _____

Flavor: _____

Flavor Type:

Sweet   Tart/Sour   Herbal   Bitter   Spicy

Flavor Strength:

Too Weak   Just Right   Too Strong

Notes: Date: ___/___/___

Caffeine: Y N

SODA CHARACTERISTICS	SCORE
Bottle Shape, Style, & Color	
Labeling Aesthetics & Description	
Aroma & Drink Color	
Carbonation / Fizziness	
Drinkability / Refreshment	
Tastes as Advertised & Expected	
Overall Flavor	
Aftertaste / Finish	
Memorability	
Value for Price	
BOTTLECAP SCORE	

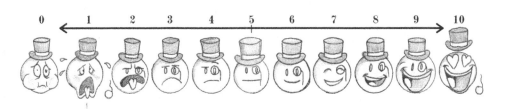

0   1   2   3   4   5   6   7   8   9   10

Brand: _____

Flavor: _____

Flavor Type:

Sweet   Tart/Sour   Herbal   Bitter   Spicy

Flavor Strength:

Too Weak   Just Right   Too Strong

Notes: Date: ___/___/___

Caffeine: Y N

SODA CHARACTERISTICS	SCORE
Bottle Shape, Style, & Color	
Labeling Aesthetics & Description	
Aroma & Drink Color	
Carbonation / Fizziness	
Drinkability / Refreshment	
Tastes as Advertised & Expected	
Overall Flavor	
Aftertaste / Finish	
Memorability	
Value for Price	
BOTTLECAP SCORE	

Brand: _____

Flavor: _____

Flavor Type:

Sweet   Tart/Sour   Herbal   Bitter   Spicy

Flavor Strength:

Too Weak   Just Right   Too Strong

Notes: Date: ___/___/___

Caffeine: Y N

SODA CHARACTERISTICS	SCORE
Bottle Shape, Style, & Color	
Labeling Aesthetics & Description	
Aroma & Drink Color	
Carbonation / Fizziness	
Drinkability / Refreshment	
Tastes as Advertised & Expected	
Overall Flavor	
Aftertaste / Finish	
Memorability	
Value for Price	
BOTTLECAP SCORE	

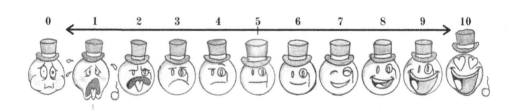

Brand: _____

Flavor: _____

Flavor Type:

Sweet   Tart/Sour   Herbal   Bitter   Spicy

Flavor Strength:

Too Weak   Just Right   Too Strong

Notes: Date: ___/___/___

Caffeine: Y N

SODA CHARACTERISTICS	SCORE
Bottle Shape, Style, & Color	
Labeling Aesthetics & Description	
Aroma & Drink Color	
Carbonation / Fizziness	
Drinkability / Refreshment	
Tastes as Advertised & Expected	
Overall Flavor	
Aftertaste / Finish	
Memorability	
Value for Price	
BOTTLECAP SCORE	

Brand: _____

Flavor: _____

Flavor Type:

Sweet   Tart/Sour   Herbal   Bitter   Spicy

Flavor Strength:

Too Weak   Just Right   Too Strong

Notes: Date: ___/___/___

Caffeine: Y N

SODA CHARACTERISTICS	SCORE
Bottle Shape, Style, & Color	
Labeling Aesthetics & Description	
Aroma & Drink Color	
Carbonation / Fizziness	
Drinkability / Refreshment	
Tastes as Advertised & Expected	
Overall Flavor	
Aftertaste / Finish	
Memorability	
Value for Price	
BOTTLECAP SCORE	

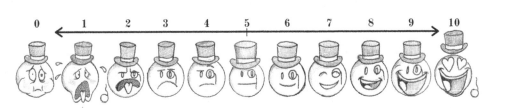

0   1   2   3   4   5   6   7   8   9   10

Brand: _____

Flavor: _____

Flavor Type:

Sweet   Tart/Sour   Herbal   Bitter   Spicy

Flavor Strength:

Too Weak   Just Right   Too Strong

Notes: Date: ___/___/___

Caffeine: Y N

SODA CHARACTERISTICS	SCORE
Bottle Shape, Style, & Color	
Labeling Aesthetics & Description	
Aroma & Drink Color	
Carbonation / Fizziness	
Drinkability / Refreshment	
Tastes as Advertised & Expected	
Overall Flavor	
Aftertaste / Finish	
Memorability	
Value for Price	
BOTTLECAP SCORE	

Brand: _____
Flavor: _____

Flavor Type:

Sweet   Tart/Sour   Herbal   Bitter   Spicy

Flavor Strength:

Too Weak   Just Right   Too Strong

Notes: Date: ___/___/___
                Caffeine: Y N

SODA CHARACTERISTICS	SCORE
Bottle Shape, Style, & Color	
Labeling Aesthetics & Description	
Aroma & Drink Color	
Carbonation / Fizziness	
Drinkability / Refreshment	
Tastes as Advertised & Expected	
Overall Flavor	
Aftertaste / Finish	
Memorability	
Value for Price	
BOTTLECAP SCORE	

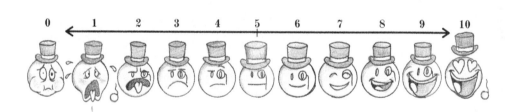

0 1 2 3 4 5 6 7 8 9 10

Brand: _____
Flavor: _____

Flavor Type:

Sweet   Tart/Sour   Herbal   Bitter   Spicy

Flavor Strength:

Too Weak   Just Right   Too Strong

Notes: Date: ___/___/___
                Caffeine: Y N

SODA CHARACTERISTICS	SCORE
Bottle Shape, Style, & Color	
Labeling Aesthetics & Description	
Aroma & Drink Color	
Carbonation / Fizziness	
Drinkability / Refreshment	
Tastes as Advertised & Expected	
Overall Flavor	
Aftertaste / Finish	
Memorability	
Value for Price	
BOTTLECAP SCORE	

Brand: _____

Flavor: _____

Flavor Type:				
Sweet	Tart/Sour	Herbal	Bitter	Spicy

Flavor Strength:

Too Weak   Just Right   Too Strong

Notes: Date: ___/___/___

Caffeine: Y N

SODA CHARACTERISTICS	SCORE
Bottle Shape, Style, & Color	
Labeling Aesthetics & Description	
Aroma & Drink Color	
Carbonation / Fizziness	
Drinkability / Refreshment	
Tastes as Advertised & Expected	
Overall Flavor	
Aftertaste / Finish	
Memorability	
Value for Price	
BOTTLECAP SCORE	

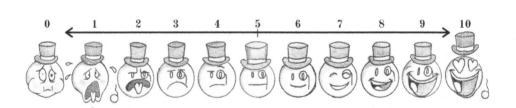

0   1   2   3   4   5   6   7   8   9   10

Brand: _____

Flavor: _____

Flavor Type:				
Sweet	Tart/Sour	Herbal	Bitter	Spicy

Flavor Strength:

Too Weak   Just Right   Too Strong

Notes: Date: ___/___/___

Caffeine: Y N

SODA CHARACTERISTICS	SCORE
Bottle Shape, Style, & Color	
Labeling Aesthetics & Description	
Aroma & Drink Color	
Carbonation / Fizziness	
Drinkability / Refreshment	
Tastes as Advertised & Expected	
Overall Flavor	
Aftertaste / Finish	
Memorability	
Value for Price	
BOTTLECAP SCORE	

Brand: _____

Flavor: _____

Flavor Type:

Sweet   Tart/Sour   Herbal   Bitter   Spicy

Flavor Strength:

Too Weak   Just Right   Too Strong

Notes: Date: ___/___/___

Caffeine: Y N

SODA CHARACTERISTICS	SCORE
Bottle Shape, Style, & Color	
Labeling Aesthetics & Description	
Aroma & Drink Color	
Carbonation / Fizziness	
Drinkability / Refreshment	
Tastes as Advertised & Expected	
Overall Flavor	
Aftertaste / Finish	
Memorability	
Value for Price	
BOTTLECAP SCORE	

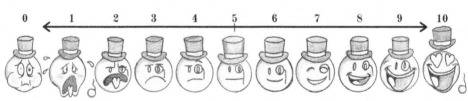

0   1   2   3   4   5   6   7   8   9   10

Brand: _____

Flavor: _____

Flavor Type:

Sweet   Tart/Sour   Herbal   Bitter   Spicy

Flavor Strength:

Too Weak   Just Right   Too Strong

Notes: Date: ___/___/___

Caffeine: Y N

SODA CHARACTERISTICS	SCORE
Bottle Shape, Style, & Color	
Labeling Aesthetics & Description	
Aroma & Drink Color	
Carbonation / Fizziness	
Drinkability / Refreshment	
Tastes as Advertised & Expected	
Overall Flavor	
Aftertaste / Finish	
Memorability	
Value for Price	
BOTTLECAP SCORE	

Brand: _____

Flavor: _____

Flavor Type:

Sweet   Tart/Sour   Herbal   Bitter   Spicy

Flavor Strength:

Too Weak   Just Right   Too Strong

Notes: Date: ___/___/___

Caffeine: Y N

SODA CHARACTERISTICS	SCORE
Bottle Shape, Style, & Color	
Labeling Aesthetics & Description	
Aroma & Drink Color	
Carbonation / Fizziness	
Drinkability / Refreshment	
Tastes as Advertised & Expected	
Overall Flavor	
Aftertaste / Finish	
Memorability	
Value for Price	
BOTTLECAP SCORE	

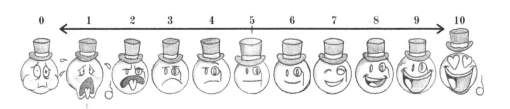

0   1   2   3   4   5   6   7   8   9   10

Brand: _____

Flavor: _____

Flavor Type:

Sweet   Tart/Sour   Herbal   Bitter   Spicy

Flavor Strength:

Too Weak   Just Right   Too Strong

Notes: Date: ___/___/___

Caffeine: Y N

SODA CHARACTERISTICS	SCORE
Bottle Shape, Style, & Color	
Labeling Aesthetics & Description	
Aroma & Drink Color	
Carbonation / Fizziness	
Drinkability / Refreshment	
Tastes as Advertised & Expected	
Overall Flavor	
Aftertaste / Finish	
Memorability	
Value for Price	
BOTTLECAP SCORE	

Brand: _____

Flavor: _____

Flavor Type:

Sweet   Tart/Sour   Herbal   Bitter   Spicy

Flavor Strength:

Too Weak   Just Right   Too Strong

Notes: Date: ___/___/___

                    Caffeine: Y N

SODA CHARACTERISTICS	SCORE
Bottle Shape, Style, & Color	
Labeling Aesthetics & Description	
Aroma & Drink Color	
Carbonation / Fizziness	
Drinkability / Refreshment	
Tastes as Advertised & Expected	
Overall Flavor	
Aftertaste / Finish	
Memorability	
Value for Price	
BOTTLECAP SCORE	

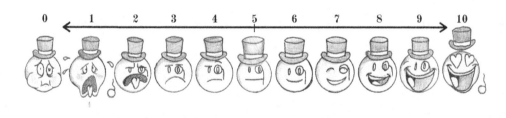

0   1   2   3   4   5   6   7   8   9   10

Brand: _____

Flavor: _____

Flavor Type:

Sweet   Tart/Sour   Herbal   Bitter   Spicy

Flavor Strength:

Too Weak   Just Right   Too Strong

Notes: Date: ___/___/___

                    Caffeine: Y N

SODA CHARACTERISTICS	SCORE
Bottle Shape, Style, & Color	
Labeling Aesthetics & Description	
Aroma & Drink Color	
Carbonation / Fizziness	
Drinkability / Refreshment	
Tastes as Advertised & Expected	
Overall Flavor	
Aftertaste / Finish	
Memorability	
Value for Price	
BOTTLECAP SCORE	

Brand: _____

Flavor: _____

Flavor Type:				
Sweet	Tart/Sour	Herbal	Bitter	Spicy

Flavor Strength:

Too Weak | Just Right | Too Strong

Notes: Date: ___/___/___

Caffeine: Y N

SODA CHARACTERISTICS	SCORE
Bottle Shape, Style, & Color	
Labeling Aesthetics & Description	
Aroma & Drink Color	
Carbonation / Fizziness	
Drinkability / Refreshment	
Tastes as Advertised & Expected	
Overall Flavor	
Aftertaste / Finish	
Memorability	
Value for Price	
BOTTLECAP SCORE	

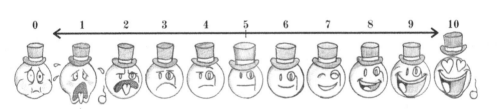

0   1   2   3   4   5   6   7   8   9   10

Brand: _____

Flavor: _____

Flavor Type:				
Sweet	Tart/Sour	Herbal	Bitter	Spicy

Flavor Strength:

Too Weak | Just Right | Too Strong

Notes: Date: ___/___/___

Caffeine: Y N

SODA CHARACTERISTICS	SCORE
Bottle Shape, Style, & Color	
Labeling Aesthetics & Description	
Aroma & Drink Color	
Carbonation / Fizziness	
Drinkability / Refreshment	
Tastes as Advertised & Expected	
Overall Flavor	
Aftertaste / Finish	
Memorability	
Value for Price	
BOTTLECAP SCORE	

DIET & LOW-CALORIE SODAS

Brand	Flavor	Score	Notes	Page
				111
				111
				112
				112
				113
				113
				114
				114
				115
				115
				116
				116
				117
				117
				118
				118
				119
				119
				120
				120
				121
				121
				122
				122
				123
				123

Brand: _____

Flavor: _____

Flavor Type:				
Sweet	Tart/Sour	Herbal	Bitter	Spicy

Flavor Strength:

Too Weak — Just Right — Too Strong

Notes:

Date: ___/___/___

Caffeine: Y N

SODA CHARACTERISTICS	SCORE
Bottle Shape, Style, & Color	
Labeling Aesthetics & Description	
Aroma & Drink Color	
Carbonation / Fizziness	
Drinkability / Refreshment	
Tastes as Advertised & Expected	
Overall Flavor	
Aftertaste / Finish	
Memorability	
Value for Price	
BOTTLECAP SCORE	

0 1 2 3 4 5 6 7 8 9 10

Brand: _____

Flavor: _____

Flavor Type:				
Sweet	Tart/Sour	Herbal	Bitter	Spicy

Flavor Strength:

Too Weak — Just Right — Too Strong

Notes:

Date: ___/___/___

Caffeine: Y N

SODA CHARACTERISTICS	SCORE
Bottle Shape, Style, & Color	
Labeling Aesthetics & Description	
Aroma & Drink Color	
Carbonation / Fizziness	
Drinkability / Refreshment	
Tastes as Advertised & Expected	
Overall Flavor	
Aftertaste / Finish	
Memorability	
Value for Price	
BOTTLECAP SCORE	

Brand: _____

Flavor: _____

Flavor Type:

Sweet   Tart/Sour   Herbal   Bitter   Spicy

Flavor Strength:

Too Weak   Just Right   Too Strong

Notes: Date: __/__/__

Caffeine: Y N

SODA CHARACTERISTICS	SCORE
Bottle Shape, Style, & Color	
Labeling Aesthetics & Description	
Aroma & Drink Color	
Carbonation / Fizziness	
Drinkability / Refreshment	
Tastes as Advertised & Expected	
Overall Flavor	
Aftertaste / Finish	
Memorability	
Value for Price	
BOTTLECAP SCORE	

0   1   2   3   4   5   6   7   8   9   10

Brand: _____

Flavor: _____

Flavor Type:

Sweet   Tart/Sour   Herbal   Bitter   Spicy

Flavor Strength:

Too Weak   Just Right   Too Strong

Notes: Date: __/__/__

Caffeine: Y N

SODA CHARACTERISTICS	SCORE
Bottle Shape, Style, & Color	
Labeling Aesthetics & Description	
Aroma & Drink Color	
Carbonation / Fizziness	
Drinkability / Refreshment	
Tastes as Advertised & Expected	
Overall Flavor	
Aftertaste / Finish	
Memorability	
Value for Price	
BOTTLECAP SCORE	

Brand: _____

Flavor: _____

Flavor Type:

Sweet   Tart/Sour   Herbal   Bitter   Spicy

Flavor Strength:

Too Weak   Just Right   Too Strong

Notes: Date: ___/___/___

Caffeine: Y   N

SODA CHARACTERISTICS	SCORE
Bottle Shape, Style, & Color	
Labeling Aesthetics & Description	
Aroma & Drink Color	
Carbonation / Fizziness	
Drinkability / Refreshment	
Tastes as Advertised & Expected	
Overall Flavor	
Aftertaste / Finish	
Memorability	
Value for Price	
BOTTLECAP SCORE	

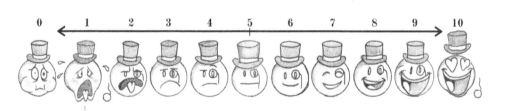

0   1   2   3   4   5   6   7   8   9   10

Brand: _____

Flavor: _____

Flavor Type:

Sweet   Tart/Sour   Herbal   Bitter   Spicy

Flavor Strength:

Too Weak   Just Right   Too Strong

Notes: Date: ___/___/___

Caffeine: Y   N

SODA CHARACTERISTICS	SCORE
Bottle Shape, Style, & Color	
Labeling Aesthetics & Description	
Aroma & Drink Color	
Carbonation / Fizziness	
Drinkability / Refreshment	
Tastes as Advertised & Expected	
Overall Flavor	
Aftertaste / Finish	
Memorability	
Value for Price	
BOTTLECAP SCORE	

Brand: _____

Flavor: _____

Flavor Type:

Sweet   Tart/Sour   Herbal   Bitter   Spicy

Flavor Strength:

Too Weak   Just Right   Too Strong

Notes: Date: ___/___/___

Caffeine: Y N

SODA CHARACTERISTICS	SCORE
Bottle Shape, Style, & Color	
Labeling Aesthetics & Description	
Aroma & Drink Color	
Carbonation / Fizziness	
Drinkability / Refreshment	
Tastes as Advertised & Expected	
Overall Flavor	
Aftertaste / Finish	
Memorability	
Value for Price	
BOTTLECAP SCORE	

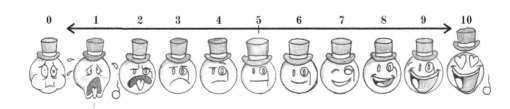

0   1   2   3   4   5   6   7   8   9   10

Brand: _____

Flavor: _____

Flavor Type:

Sweet   Tart/Sour   Herbal   Bitter   Spicy

Flavor Strength:

Too Weak   Just Right   Too Strong

Notes: Date: ___/___/___

Caffeine: Y N

SODA CHARACTERISTICS	SCORE
Bottle Shape, Style, & Color	
Labeling Aesthetics & Description	
Aroma & Drink Color	
Carbonation / Fizziness	
Drinkability / Refreshment	
Tastes as Advertised & Expected	
Overall Flavor	
Aftertaste / Finish	
Memorability	
Value for Price	
BOTTLECAP SCORE	

DIET & LOW-CALORIE SODAS

Brand: _____

Flavor: _____

Flavor Type:

Sweet   Tart/Sour   Herbal   Bitter   Spicy

Flavor Strength:

Too Weak   Just Right   Too Strong

Notes: Date: ___/___/___

Caffeine: Y N

SODA CHARACTERISTICS	SCORE
Bottle Shape, Style, & Color	
Labeling Aesthetics & Description	
Aroma & Drink Color	
Carbonation / Fizziness	
Drinkability / Refreshment	
Tastes as Advertised & Expected	
Overall Flavor	
Aftertaste / Finish	
Memorability	
Value for Price	
BOTTLECAP SCORE	

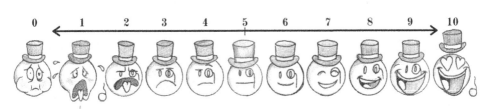

0   1   2   3   4   5   6   7   8   9   10

Brand: _____

Flavor: _____

Flavor Type:

Sweet   Tart/Sour   Herbal   Bitter   Spicy

Flavor Strength:

Too Weak   Just Right   Too Strong

Notes: Date: ___/___/___

Caffeine: Y N

SODA CHARACTERISTICS	SCORE
Bottle Shape, Style, & Color	
Labeling Aesthetics & Description	
Aroma & Drink Color	
Carbonation / Fizziness	
Drinkability / Refreshment	
Tastes as Advertised & Expected	
Overall Flavor	
Aftertaste / Finish	
Memorability	
Value for Price	
BOTTLECAP SCORE	

Brand: _____

Flavor: _____

Flavor Type:

Sweet   Tart/Sour   Herbal   Bitter   Spicy

Flavor Strength:

Too Weak   Just Right   Too Strong

Notes: Date: ___/___/___

Caffeine: Y N

SODA CHARACTERISTICS	SCORE
Bottle Shape, Style, & Color	
Labeling Aesthetics & Description	
Aroma & Drink Color	
Carbonation / Fizziness	
Drinkability / Refreshment	
Tastes as Advertised & Expected	
Overall Flavor	
Aftertaste / Finish	
Memorability	
Value for Price	
BOTTLECAP SCORE	

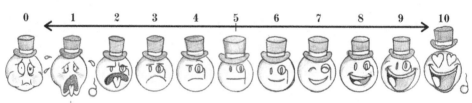

0   1   2   3   4   5   6   7   8   9   10

Brand: _____

Flavor: _____

Flavor Type:

Sweet   Tart/Sour   Herbal   Bitter   Spicy

Flavor Strength:

Too Weak   Just Right   Too Strong

Notes: Date: ___/___/___

Caffeine: Y N

SODA CHARACTERISTICS	SCORE
Bottle Shape, Style, & Color	
Labeling Aesthetics & Description	
Aroma & Drink Color	
Carbonation / Fizziness	
Drinkability / Refreshment	
Tastes as Advertised & Expected	
Overall Flavor	
Aftertaste / Finish	
Memorability	
Value for Price	
BOTTLECAP SCORE	

Brand: _____

Flavor: _____

Flavor Type:

Sweet   Tart/Sour   Herbal   Bitter   Spicy

Flavor Strength:

Too Weak   Just Right   Too Strong

Notes: Date: ___/___/___

Caffeine: Y N

SODA CHARACTERISTICS	SCORE
Bottle Shape, Style, & Color	
Labeling Aesthetics & Description	
Aroma & Drink Color	
Carbonation / Fizziness	
Drinkability / Refreshment	
Tastes as Advertised & Expected	
Overall Flavor	
Aftertaste / Finish	
Memorability	
Value for Price	
BOTTLECAP SCORE	

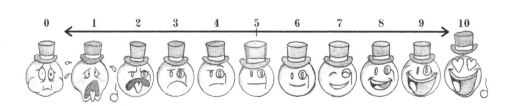

0   1   2   3   4   5   6   7   8   9   10

Brand: _____

Flavor: _____

Flavor Type:

Sweet   Tart/Sour   Herbal   Bitter   Spicy

Flavor Strength:

Too Weak   Just Right   Too Strong

Notes: Date: ___/___/___

Caffeine: Y N

SODA CHARACTERISTICS	SCORE
Bottle Shape, Style, & Color	
Labeling Aesthetics & Description	
Aroma & Drink Color	
Carbonation / Fizziness	
Drinkability / Refreshment	
Tastes as Advertised & Expected	
Overall Flavor	
Aftertaste / Finish	
Memorability	
Value for Price	
BOTTLECAP SCORE	

Brand: _____

Flavor: _____

Flavor Type:

Sweet   Tart/Sour   Herbal   Bitter   Spicy

Flavor Strength:

Too Weak   Just Right   Too Strong

Notes: Date: ___/___/___

Caffeine: Y N

SODA CHARACTERISTICS	SCORE
Bottle Shape, Style, & Color	
Labeling Aesthetics & Description	
Aroma & Drink Color	
Carbonation / Fizziness	
Drinkability / Refreshment	
Tastes as Advertised & Expected	
Overall Flavor	
Aftertaste / Finish	
Memorability	
Value for Price	
BOTTLECAP SCORE	

0   1   2   3   4   5   6   7   8   9   10

Brand: _____

Flavor: _____

Flavor Type:

Sweet   Tart/Sour   Herbal   Bitter   Spicy

Flavor Strength:

Too Weak   Just Right   Too Strong

Notes: Date: ___/___/___

Caffeine: Y N

SODA CHARACTERISTICS	SCORE
Bottle Shape, Style, & Color	
Labeling Aesthetics & Description	
Aroma & Drink Color	
Carbonation / Fizziness	
Drinkability / Refreshment	
Tastes as Advertised & Expected	
Overall Flavor	
Aftertaste / Finish	
Memorability	
Value for Price	
BOTTLECAP SCORE	

Brand: _____

Flavor: _____

Flavor Type:

Sweet   Tart/Sour   Herbal   Bitter   Spicy

Flavor Strength:

Too Weak   Just Right   Too Strong

Notes: Date: ___/___/___

Caffeine: Y   N

SODA CHARACTERISTICS	SCORE
Bottle Shape, Style, & Color	
Labeling Aesthetics & Description	
Aroma & Drink Color	
Carbonation / Fizziness	
Drinkability / Refreshment	
Tastes as Advertised & Expected	
Overall Flavor	
Aftertaste / Finish	
Memorability	
Value for Price	
BOTTLECAP SCORE	

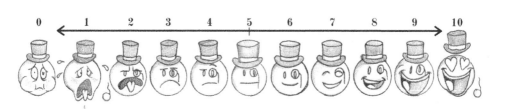

0   1   2   3   4   5   6   7   8   9   10

Brand: _____

Flavor: _____

Flavor Type:

Sweet   Tart/Sour   Herbal   Bitter   Spicy

Flavor Strength:

Too Weak   Just Right   Too Strong

Notes: Date: ___/___/___

Caffeine: Y   N

SODA CHARACTERISTICS	SCORE
Bottle Shape, Style, & Color	
Labeling Aesthetics & Description	
Aroma & Drink Color	
Carbonation / Fizziness	
Drinkability / Refreshment	
Tastes as Advertised & Expected	
Overall Flavor	
Aftertaste / Finish	
Memorability	
Value for Price	
BOTTLECAP SCORE	

Brand: _____

Flavor: _____

Flavor Type:

Sweet   Tart/Sour   Herbal   Bitter   Spicy

Flavor Strength:

Too Weak   Just Right   Too Strong

Notes: Date: ___/___/___

Caffeine: Y N

SODA CHARACTERISTICS	SCORE
Bottle Shape, Style, & Color	
Labeling Aesthetics & Description	
Aroma & Drink Color	
Carbonation / Fizziness	
Drinkability / Refreshment	
Tastes as Advertised & Expected	
Overall Flavor	
Aftertaste / Finish	
Memorability	
Value for Price	
BOTTLECAP SCORE	

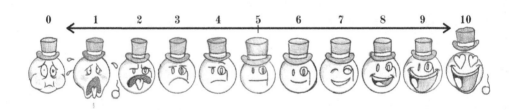

0   1   2   3   4   5   6   7   8   9   10

Brand: _____

Flavor: _____

Flavor Type:

Sweet   Tart/Sour   Herbal   Bitter   Spicy

Flavor Strength:

Too Weak   Just Right   Too Strong

Notes: Date: ___/___/___

Caffeine: Y N

SODA CHARACTERISTICS	SCORE
Bottle Shape, Style, & Color	
Labeling Aesthetics & Description	
Aroma & Drink Color	
Carbonation / Fizziness	
Drinkability / Refreshment	
Tastes as Advertised & Expected	
Overall Flavor	
Aftertaste / Finish	
Memorability	
Value for Price	
BOTTLECAP SCORE	

Brand: _____

Flavor: _____

Flavor Type:

Sweet   Tart/Sour   Herbal   Bitter   Spicy

Flavor Strength:

Too Weak   Just Right   Too Strong

Notes: Date: ___/___/___

Caffeine: Y   N

SODA CHARACTERISTICS	SCORE
Bottle Shape, Style, & Color	
Labeling Aesthetics & Description	
Aroma & Drink Color	
Carbonation / Fizziness	
Drinkability / Refreshment	
Tastes as Advertised & Expected	
Overall Flavor	
Aftertaste / Finish	
Memorability	
Value for Price	
BOTTLECAP SCORE	

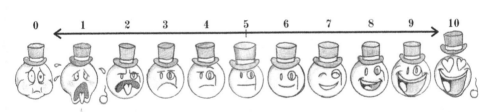

0   1   2   3   4   5   6   7   8   9   10

Brand: _____

Flavor: _____

Flavor Type:

Sweet   Tart/Sour   Herbal   Bitter   Spicy

Flavor Strength:

Too Weak   Just Right   Too Strong

Notes: Date: ___/___/___

Caffeine: Y   N

SODA CHARACTERISTICS	SCORE
Bottle Shape, Style, & Color	
Labeling Aesthetics & Description	
Aroma & Drink Color	
Carbonation / Fizziness	
Drinkability / Refreshment	
Tastes as Advertised & Expected	
Overall Flavor	
Aftertaste / Finish	
Memorability	
Value for Price	
BOTTLECAP SCORE	

Brand: _____

Flavor: _____

Flavor Type:

Sweet   Tart/Sour   Herbal   Bitter   Spicy

Flavor Strength:

Too Weak   Just Right   Too Strong

Notes: Date: ___/___/___

Caffeine: Y   N

SODA CHARACTERISTICS	SCORE
Bottle Shape, Style, & Color	
Labeling Aesthetics & Description	
Aroma & Drink Color	
Carbonation / Fizziness	
Drinkability / Refreshment	
Tastes as Advertised & Expected	
Overall Flavor	
Aftertaste / Finish	
Memorability	
Value for Price	
BOTTLECAP SCORE	

0   1   2   3   4   5   6   7   8   9   10

Brand: _____

Flavor: _____

Flavor Type:

Sweet   Tart/Sour   Herbal   Bitter   Spicy

Flavor Strength:

Too Weak   Just Right   Too Strong

Notes: Date: ___/___/___

Caffeine: Y   N

SODA CHARACTERISTICS	SCORE
Bottle Shape, Style, & Color	
Labeling Aesthetics & Description	
Aroma & Drink Color	
Carbonation / Fizziness	
Drinkability / Refreshment	
Tastes as Advertised & Expected	
Overall Flavor	
Aftertaste / Finish	
Memorability	
Value for Price	
BOTTLECAP SCORE	

Brand: _____

Flavor: _____

Flavor Type:

Sweet   Tart/Sour   Herbal   Bitter   Spicy

Flavor Strength:

Too Weak   Just Right   Too Strong

Notes: Date: ___/___/___

Caffeine: Y N

SODA CHARACTERISTICS	SCORE
Bottle Shape, Style, & Color	
Labeling Aesthetics & Description	
Aroma & Drink Color	
Carbonation / Fizziness	
Drinkability / Refreshment	
Tastes as Advertised & Expected	
Overall Flavor	
Aftertaste / Finish	
Memorability	
Value for Price	
BOTTLECAP SCORE	

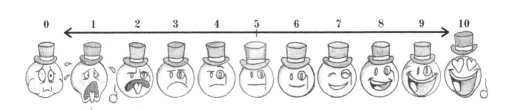

0   1   2   3   4   5   6   7   8   9   10

Brand: _____

Flavor: _____

Flavor Type:

Sweet   Tart/Sour   Herbal   Bitter   Spicy

Flavor Strength:

Too Weak   Just Right   Too Strong

Notes: Date: ___/___/___

Caffeine: Y N

SODA CHARACTERISTICS	SCORE
Bottle Shape, Style, & Color	
Labeling Aesthetics & Description	
Aroma & Drink Color	
Carbonation / Fizziness	
Drinkability / Refreshment	
Tastes as Advertised & Expected	
Overall Flavor	
Aftertaste / Finish	
Memorability	
Value for Price	
BOTTLECAP SCORE	

FRUIT FLAVORS

DOES NOT INCLUDE CITRUS, GRAPE, OR CHERRY FLAVORS

Brand	Flavor	Score	Notes	Page
				125
				125
				126
				126
				127
				127
				128
				128
				129
				129
				130
				130
				131
				131
				132
				132
				133
				133
				134
				134
				135
				135
				136
				136
				137
				137

Brand: _____

Flavor: _____

Flavor Type:

Sweet Tart/Sour Herbal Bitter Spicy

Flavor Strength:

Too Weak   Just Right   Too Strong

Notes: Date: ___/___/___

                    Caffeine: Y N

SODA CHARACTERISTICS	SCORE
Bottle Shape, Style, & Color	
Labeling Aesthetics & Description	
Aroma & Drink Color	
Carbonation / Fizziness	
Drinkability / Refreshment	
Tastes as Advertised & Expected	
Overall Flavor	
Aftertaste / Finish	
Memorability	
Value for Price	
BOTTLECAP SCORE	

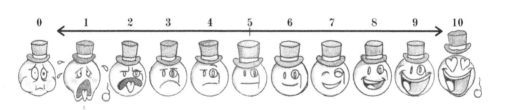

0   1   2   3   4   5   6   7   8   9   10

Brand: _____

Flavor: _____

Flavor Type:

Sweet Tart/Sour Herbal Bitter Spicy

Flavor Strength:

Too Weak   Just Right   Too Strong

Notes: Date: ___/___/___

                    Caffeine: Y N

SODA CHARACTERISTICS	SCORE
Bottle Shape, Style, & Color	
Labeling Aesthetics & Description	
Aroma & Drink Color	
Carbonation / Fizziness	
Drinkability / Refreshment	
Tastes as Advertised & Expected	
Overall Flavor	
Aftertaste / Finish	
Memorability	
Value for Price	
BOTTLECAP SCORE	

Brand: _____

Flavor: _____

Flavor Type:

Sweet   Tart/Sour   Herbal   Bitter   Spicy

Flavor Strength:

Too Weak   Just Right   Too Strong

Notes: Date: ___/___/___

Caffeine: Y   N

SODA CHARACTERISTICS	SCORE
Bottle Shape, Style, & Color	
Labeling Aesthetics & Description	
Aroma & Drink Color	
Carbonation / Fizziness	
Drinkability / Refreshment	
Tastes as Advertised & Expected	
Overall Flavor	
Aftertaste / Finish	
Memorability	
Value for Price	
BOTTLECAP SCORE	

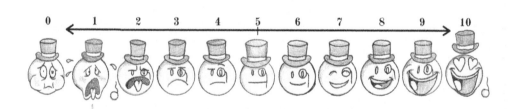

Brand: _____

Flavor: _____

Flavor Type:

Sweet   Tart/Sour   Herbal   Bitter   Spicy

Flavor Strength:

Too Weak   Just Right   Too Strong

Notes: Date: ___/___/___

Caffeine: Y   N

SODA CHARACTERISTICS	SCORE
Bottle Shape, Style, & Color	
Labeling Aesthetics & Description	
Aroma & Drink Color	
Carbonation / Fizziness	
Drinkability / Refreshment	
Tastes as Advertised & Expected	
Overall Flavor	
Aftertaste / Finish	
Memorability	
Value for Price	
BOTTLECAP SCORE	

Brand: _____

Flavor: _____

Flavor Type:				
Sweet	Tart/Sour	Herbal	Bitter	Spicy

Flavor Strength:

Too Weak   Just Right   Too Strong

Notes: Date: ___/___/___

Caffeine: Y N

SODA CHARACTERISTICS	SCORE
Bottle Shape, Style, & Color	
Labeling Aesthetics & Description	
Aroma & Drink Color	
Carbonation / Fizziness	
Drinkability / Refreshment	
Tastes as Advertised & Expected	
Overall Flavor	
Aftertaste / Finish	
Memorability	
Value for Price	
BOTTLECAP SCORE	

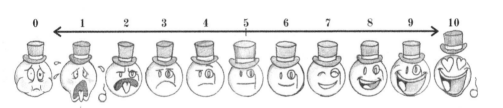

0   1   2   3   4   5   6   7   8   9   10

Brand: _____

Flavor: _____

Flavor Type:				
Sweet	Tart/Sour	Herbal	Bitter	Spicy

Flavor Strength:

Too Weak   Just Right   Too Strong

Notes: Date: ___/___/___

Caffeine: Y N

SODA CHARACTERISTICS	SCORE
Bottle Shape, Style, & Color	
Labeling Aesthetics & Description	
Aroma & Drink Color	
Carbonation / Fizziness	
Drinkability / Refreshment	
Tastes as Advertised & Expected	
Overall Flavor	
Aftertaste / Finish	
Memorability	
Value for Price	
BOTTLECAP SCORE	

Brand: _____

Flavor: _____

Flavor Type:

Sweet Tart/Sour Herbal Bitter Spicy

Flavor Strength:

Too Weak   Just Right   Too Strong

Notes: Date: ___/___/___

Caffeine: Y N

SODA CHARACTERISTICS	SCORE
Bottle Shape, Style, & Color	
Labeling Aesthetics & Description	
Aroma & Drink Color	
Carbonation / Fizziness	
Drinkability / Refreshment	
Tastes as Advertised & Expected	
Overall Flavor	
Aftertaste / Finish	
Memorability	
Value for Price	
BOTTLECAP SCORE	

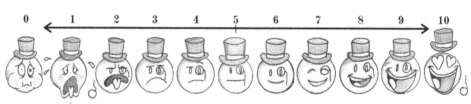

Brand: _____

Flavor: _____

Flavor Type:

Sweet Tart/Sour Herbal Bitter Spicy

Flavor Strength:

Too Weak   Just Right   Too Strong

Notes: Date: ___/___/___

Caffeine: Y N

SODA CHARACTERISTICS	SCORE
Bottle Shape, Style, & Color	
Labeling Aesthetics & Description	
Aroma & Drink Color	
Carbonation / Fizziness	
Drinkability / Refreshment	
Tastes as Advertised & Expected	
Overall Flavor	
Aftertaste / Finish	
Memorability	
Value for Price	
BOTTLECAP SCORE	

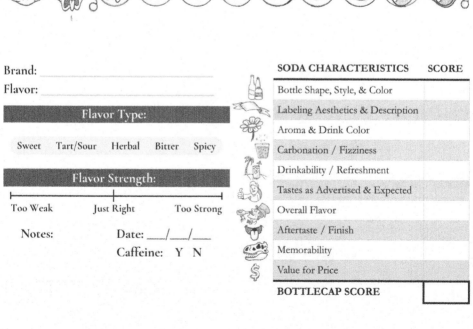

Brand: _____

Flavor: _____

Flavor Type:

Sweet   Tart/Sour   Herbal   Bitter   Spicy

Flavor Strength:

Too Weak   Just Right   Too Strong

Notes:

Date: ___/___/___

Caffeine: Y   N

SODA CHARACTERISTICS	SCORE
Bottle Shape, Style, & Color	
Labeling Aesthetics & Description	
Aroma & Drink Color	
Carbonation / Fizziness	
Drinkability / Refreshment	
Tastes as Advertised & Expected	
Overall Flavor	
Aftertaste / Finish	
Memorability	
Value for Price	
BOTTLECAP SCORE	

Brand: _____

Flavor: _____

Flavor Type:

Sweet   Tart/Sour   Herbal   Bitter   Spicy

Flavor Strength:

Too Weak   Just Right   Too Strong

Notes:

Date: ___/___/___

Caffeine: Y   N

SODA CHARACTERISTICS	SCORE
Bottle Shape, Style, & Color	
Labeling Aesthetics & Description	
Aroma & Drink Color	
Carbonation / Fizziness	
Drinkability / Refreshment	
Tastes as Advertised & Expected	
Overall Flavor	
Aftertaste / Finish	
Memorability	
Value for Price	
BOTTLECAP SCORE	

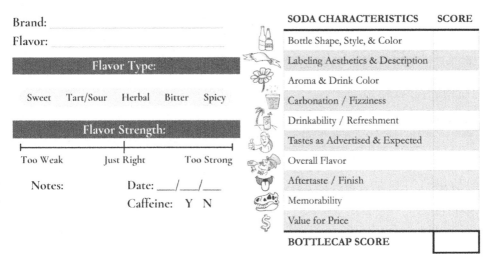

Brand: _____

Flavor: _____

Flavor Type:

Sweet   Tart/Sour   Herbal   Bitter   Spicy

Flavor Strength:

Too Weak   Just Right   Too Strong

Notes: Date: ___/___/___

Caffeine: Y   N

SODA CHARACTERISTICS	SCORE
Bottle Shape, Style, & Color	
Labeling Aesthetics & Description	
Aroma & Drink Color	
Carbonation / Fizziness	
Drinkability / Refreshment	
Tastes as Advertised & Expected	
Overall Flavor	
Aftertaste / Finish	
Memorability	
Value for Price	
BOTTLECAP SCORE	

0   1   2   3   4   5   6   7   8   9   10

Brand: _____

Flavor: _____

Flavor Type:

Sweet   Tart/Sour   Herbal   Bitter   Spicy

Flavor Strength:

Too Weak   Just Right   Too Strong

Notes: Date: ___/___/___

Caffeine: Y   N

SODA CHARACTERISTICS	SCORE
Bottle Shape, Style, & Color	
Labeling Aesthetics & Description	
Aroma & Drink Color	
Carbonation / Fizziness	
Drinkability / Refreshment	
Tastes as Advertised & Expected	
Overall Flavor	
Aftertaste / Finish	
Memorability	
Value for Price	
BOTTLECAP SCORE	

Brand: _____

Flavor: _____

Flavor Type:

Sweet   Tart/Sour   Herbal   Bitter   Spicy

Flavor Strength:

Too Weak   Just Right   Too Strong

Notes: Date: ___/___/___

Caffeine: Y N

SODA CHARACTERISTICS	SCORE
Bottle Shape, Style, & Color	
Labeling Aesthetics & Description	
Aroma & Drink Color	
Carbonation / Fizziness	
Drinkability / Refreshment	
Tastes as Advertised & Expected	
Overall Flavor	
Aftertaste / Finish	
Memorability	
Value for Price	
BOTTLECAP SCORE	

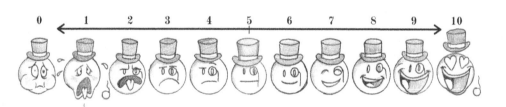

0   1   2   3   4   5   6   7   8   9   10

Brand: _____

Flavor: _____

Flavor Type:

Sweet   Tart/Sour   Herbal   Bitter   Spicy

Flavor Strength:

Too Weak   Just Right   Too Strong

Notes: Date: ___/___/___

Caffeine: Y N

SODA CHARACTERISTICS	SCORE
Bottle Shape, Style, & Color	
Labeling Aesthetics & Description	
Aroma & Drink Color	
Carbonation / Fizziness	
Drinkability / Refreshment	
Tastes as Advertised & Expected	
Overall Flavor	
Aftertaste / Finish	
Memorability	
Value for Price	
BOTTLECAP SCORE	

Brand: _____

Flavor: _____

Flavor Type:

Sweet   Tart/Sour   Herbal   Bitter   Spicy

Flavor Strength:

Too Weak   Just Right   Too Strong

Notes: Date: ___/___/___

Caffeine: Y   N

SODA CHARACTERISTICS	SCORE
Bottle Shape, Style, & Color	
Labeling Aesthetics & Description	
Aroma & Drink Color	
Carbonation / Fizziness	
Drinkability / Refreshment	
Tastes as Advertised & Expected	
Overall Flavor	
Aftertaste / Finish	
Memorability	
Value for Price	
BOTTLECAP SCORE	

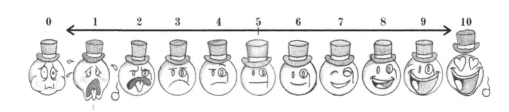

0   1   2   3   4   5   6   7   8   9   10

Brand: _____

Flavor: _____

Flavor Type:

Sweet   Tart/Sour   Herbal   Bitter   Spicy

Flavor Strength:

Too Weak   Just Right   Too Strong

Notes: Date: ___/___/___

Caffeine: Y   N

SODA CHARACTERISTICS	SCORE
Bottle Shape, Style, & Color	
Labeling Aesthetics & Description	
Aroma & Drink Color	
Carbonation / Fizziness	
Drinkability / Refreshment	
Tastes as Advertised & Expected	
Overall Flavor	
Aftertaste / Finish	
Memorability	
Value for Price	
BOTTLECAP SCORE	

Brand: _____

Flavor: _____

Flavor Type:

Sweet   Tart/Sour   Herbal   Bitter   Spicy

Flavor Strength:

Too Weak   Just Right   Too Strong

Notes: Date: ___/___/___

Caffeine: Y   N

SODA CHARACTERISTICS	SCORE
Bottle Shape, Style, & Color	
Labeling Aesthetics & Description	
Aroma & Drink Color	
Carbonation / Fizziness	
Drinkability / Refreshment	
Tastes as Advertised & Expected	
Overall Flavor	
Aftertaste / Finish	
Memorability	
Value for Price	
BOTTLECAP SCORE	

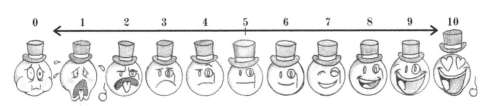

0   1   2   3   4   5   6   7   8   9   10

Brand: _____

Flavor: _____

Flavor Type:

Sweet   Tart/Sour   Herbal   Bitter   Spicy

Flavor Strength:

Too Weak   Just Right   Too Strong

Notes: Date: ___/___/___

Caffeine: Y   N

SODA CHARACTERISTICS	SCORE
Bottle Shape, Style, & Color	
Labeling Aesthetics & Description	
Aroma & Drink Color	
Carbonation / Fizziness	
Drinkability / Refreshment	
Tastes as Advertised & Expected	
Overall Flavor	
Aftertaste / Finish	
Memorability	
Value for Price	
BOTTLECAP SCORE	

Brand: _____

Flavor: _____

Flavor Type:

Sweet   Tart/Sour   Herbal   Bitter   Spicy

Flavor Strength:

Too Weak   Just Right   Too Strong

Notes: Date: ___/___/___

Caffeine: Y N

SODA CHARACTERISTICS	SCORE
Bottle Shape, Style, & Color	
Labeling Aesthetics & Description	
Aroma & Drink Color	
Carbonation / Fizziness	
Drinkability / Refreshment	
Tastes as Advertised & Expected	
Overall Flavor	
Aftertaste / Finish	
Memorability	
Value for Price	
BOTTLECAP SCORE	

Brand: _____

Flavor: _____

Flavor Type:

Sweet   Tart/Sour   Herbal   Bitter   Spicy

Flavor Strength:

Too Weak   Just Right   Too Strong

Notes: Date: ___/___/___

Caffeine: Y N

SODA CHARACTERISTICS	SCORE
Bottle Shape, Style, & Color	
Labeling Aesthetics & Description	
Aroma & Drink Color	
Carbonation / Fizziness	
Drinkability / Refreshment	
Tastes as Advertised & Expected	
Overall Flavor	
Aftertaste / Finish	
Memorability	
Value for Price	
BOTTLECAP SCORE	

Brand: _____

Flavor: _____

Flavor Type:

Sweet   Tart/Sour   Herbal   Bitter   Spicy

Flavor Strength:

Too Weak   Just Right   Too Strong

Notes: Date: ___/___/___

Caffeine: Y   N

SODA CHARACTERISTICS	SCORE
Bottle Shape, Style, & Color	
Labeling Aesthetics & Description	
Aroma & Drink Color	
Carbonation / Fizziness	
Drinkability / Refreshment	
Tastes as Advertised & Expected	
Overall Flavor	
Aftertaste / Finish	
Memorability	
Value for Price	
BOTTLECAP SCORE	

0   1   2   3   4   5   6   7   8   9   10

Brand: _____

Flavor: _____

Flavor Type:

Sweet   Tart/Sour   Herbal   Bitter   Spicy

Flavor Strength:

Too Weak   Just Right   Too Strong

Notes: Date: ___/___/___

Caffeine: Y   N

SODA CHARACTERISTICS	SCORE
Bottle Shape, Style, & Color	
Labeling Aesthetics & Description	
Aroma & Drink Color	
Carbonation / Fizziness	
Drinkability / Refreshment	
Tastes as Advertised & Expected	
Overall Flavor	
Aftertaste / Finish	
Memorability	
Value for Price	
BOTTLECAP SCORE	

Brand: _____

Flavor: _____

Flavor Type:

Sweet   Tart/Sour   Herbal   Bitter   Spicy

Flavor Strength:

Too Weak   Just Right   Too Strong

Notes: Date: ___/___/___

                Caffeine: Y   N

SODA CHARACTERISTICS	SCORE
Bottle Shape, Style, & Color	
Labeling Aesthetics & Description	
Aroma & Drink Color	
Carbonation / Fizziness	
Drinkability / Refreshment	
Tastes as Advertised & Expected	
Overall Flavor	
Aftertaste / Finish	
Memorability	
Value for Price	
BOTTLECAP SCORE	

0   1   2   3   4   5   6   7   8   9   10

Brand: _____

Flavor: _____

Flavor Type:

Sweet   Tart/Sour   Herbal   Bitter   Spicy

Flavor Strength:

Too Weak   Just Right   Too Strong

Notes: Date: ___/___/___

                Caffeine: Y   N

SODA CHARACTERISTICS	SCORE
Bottle Shape, Style, & Color	
Labeling Aesthetics & Description	
Aroma & Drink Color	
Carbonation / Fizziness	
Drinkability / Refreshment	
Tastes as Advertised & Expected	
Overall Flavor	
Aftertaste / Finish	
Memorability	
Value for Price	
BOTTLECAP SCORE	

Brand: _____

Flavor: _____

Flavor Type:

Sweet   Tart/Sour   Herbal   Bitter   Spicy

Flavor Strength:

Too Weak   Just Right   Too Strong

Notes: Date: ___/___/___

Caffeine: Y   N

SODA CHARACTERISTICS	SCORE
Bottle Shape, Style, & Color	
Labeling Aesthetics & Description	
Aroma & Drink Color	
Carbonation / Fizziness	
Drinkability / Refreshment	
Tastes as Advertised & Expected	
Overall Flavor	
Aftertaste / Finish	
Memorability	
Value for Price	
BOTTLECAP SCORE	

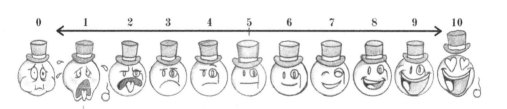

0   1   2   3   4   5   6   7   8   9   10

Brand: _____

Flavor: _____

Flavor Type:

Sweet   Tart/Sour   Herbal   Bitter   Spicy

Flavor Strength:

Too Weak   Just Right   Too Strong

Notes: Date: ___/___/___

Caffeine: Y   N

SODA CHARACTERISTICS	SCORE
Bottle Shape, Style, & Color	
Labeling Aesthetics & Description	
Aroma & Drink Color	
Carbonation / Fizziness	
Drinkability / Refreshment	
Tastes as Advertised & Expected	
Overall Flavor	
Aftertaste / Finish	
Memorability	
Value for Price	
BOTTLECAP SCORE	

GINGER ALE & GINGER BEER FLAVORS

Brand	Flavor	Score	Notes	Page
				139
				139
				140
				140
				141
				141
				142
				142
				143
				143
				144
				144
				145
				145
				146
				146
				147
				147
				148
				148
				149
				149
				150
				150
				151
				151

GINGER ALE & GINGER BEER FLAVORS

Brand: _____

Flavor: _____

Flavor Type:

Sweet   Tart/Sour   Herbal   Bitter   Spicy

Flavor Strength:

Too Weak   Just Right   Too Strong

Notes: Date: ___/___/___

Caffeine: Y   N

SODA CHARACTERISTICS	SCORE
Bottle Shape, Style, & Color	
Labeling Aesthetics & Description	
Aroma & Drink Color	
Carbonation / Fizziness	
Drinkability / Refreshment	
Tastes as Advertised & Expected	
Overall Flavor	
Aftertaste / Finish	
Memorability	
Value for Price	
BOTTLECAP SCORE	

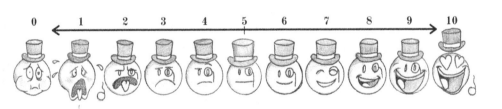

0   1   2   3   4   5   6   7   8   9   10

Brand: _____

Flavor: _____

Flavor Type:

Sweet   Tart/Sour   Herbal   Bitter   Spicy

Flavor Strength:

Too Weak   Just Right   Too Strong

Notes: Date: ___/___/___

Caffeine: Y   N

SODA CHARACTERISTICS	SCORE
Bottle Shape, Style, & Color	
Labeling Aesthetics & Description	
Aroma & Drink Color	
Carbonation / Fizziness	
Drinkability / Refreshment	
Tastes as Advertised & Expected	
Overall Flavor	
Aftertaste / Finish	
Memorability	
Value for Price	
BOTTLECAP SCORE	

Brand: _____

Flavor: _____

Flavor Type:

Sweet   Tart/Sour   Herbal   Bitter   Spicy

Flavor Strength:

Too Weak   Just Right   Too Strong

Notes: Date: ___/___/___

Caffeine: Y N

SODA CHARACTERISTICS	SCORE
Bottle Shape, Style, & Color	
Labeling Aesthetics & Description	
Aroma & Drink Color	
Carbonation / Fizziness	
Drinkability / Refreshment	
Tastes as Advertised & Expected	
Overall Flavor	
Aftertaste / Finish	
Memorability	
Value for Price	
BOTTLECAP SCORE	

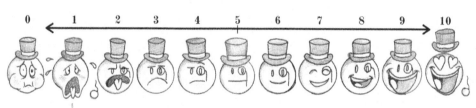

0   1   2   3   4   5   6   7   8   9   10

Brand: _____

Flavor: _____

Flavor Type:

Sweet   Tart/Sour   Herbal   Bitter   Spicy

Flavor Strength:

Too Weak   Just Right   Too Strong

Notes: Date: ___/___/___

Caffeine: Y N

SODA CHARACTERISTICS	SCORE
Bottle Shape, Style, & Color	
Labeling Aesthetics & Description	
Aroma & Drink Color	
Carbonation / Fizziness	
Drinkability / Refreshment	
Tastes as Advertised & Expected	
Overall Flavor	
Aftertaste / Finish	
Memorability	
Value for Price	
BOTTLECAP SCORE	

GINGER ALE & GINGER BEER FLAVORS

Brand: _____

Flavor: _____

Flavor Type:

Sweet   Tart/Sour   Herbal   Bitter   Spicy

Flavor Strength:

Too Weak   Just Right   Too Strong

Notes: Date: ___/___/___

                    Caffeine: Y   N

SODA CHARACTERISTICS	SCORE
Bottle Shape, Style, & Color	
Labeling Aesthetics & Description	
Aroma & Drink Color	
Carbonation / Fizziness	
Drinkability / Refreshment	
Tastes as Advertised & Expected	
Overall Flavor	
Aftertaste / Finish	
Memorability	
Value for Price	
BOTTLECAP SCORE	

Brand: _____

Flavor: _____

Flavor Type:

Sweet   Tart/Sour   Herbal   Bitter   Spicy

Flavor Strength:

Too Weak   Just Right   Too Strong

Notes: Date: ___/___/___

                    Caffeine: Y   N

SODA CHARACTERISTICS	SCORE
Bottle Shape, Style, & Color	
Labeling Aesthetics & Description	
Aroma & Drink Color	
Carbonation / Fizziness	
Drinkability / Refreshment	
Tastes as Advertised & Expected	
Overall Flavor	
Aftertaste / Finish	
Memorability	
Value for Price	
BOTTLECAP SCORE	

Brand: _____

Flavor: _____

Flavor Type:

Sweet   Tart/Sour   Herbal   Bitter   Spicy

Flavor Strength:

Too Weak   Just Right   Too Strong

Notes: Date: ___/___/___

Caffeine: Y N

SODA CHARACTERISTICS	SCORE
Bottle Shape, Style, & Color	
Labeling Aesthetics & Description	
Aroma & Drink Color	
Carbonation / Fizziness	
Drinkability / Refreshment	
Tastes as Advertised & Expected	
Overall Flavor	
Aftertaste / Finish	
Memorability	
Value for Price	
BOTTLECAP SCORE	

0 1 2 3 4 5 6 7 8 9 10

Brand: _____

Flavor: _____

Flavor Type:

Sweet   Tart/Sour   Herbal   Bitter   Spicy

Flavor Strength:

Too Weak   Just Right   Too Strong

Notes: Date: ___/___/___

Caffeine: Y N

SODA CHARACTERISTICS	SCORE
Bottle Shape, Style, & Color	
Labeling Aesthetics & Description	
Aroma & Drink Color	
Carbonation / Fizziness	
Drinkability / Refreshment	
Tastes as Advertised & Expected	
Overall Flavor	
Aftertaste / Finish	
Memorability	
Value for Price	
BOTTLECAP SCORE	

GINGER ALE & GINGER BEER FLAVORS

Brand: _____

Flavor: _____

Flavor Type:

Sweet   Tart/Sour   Herbal   Bitter   Spicy

Flavor Strength:

Too Weak   Just Right   Too Strong

Notes: Date: ___/___/___

Caffeine: Y N

SODA CHARACTERISTICS	SCORE
Bottle Shape, Style, & Color	
Labeling Aesthetics & Description	
Aroma & Drink Color	
Carbonation / Fizziness	
Drinkability / Refreshment	
Tastes as Advertised & Expected	
Overall Flavor	
Aftertaste / Finish	
Memorability	
Value for Price	
BOTTLECAP SCORE	

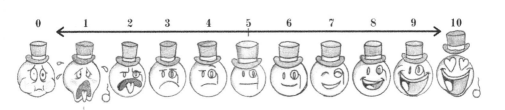

0   1   2   3   4   5   6   7   8   9   10

Brand: _____

Flavor: _____

Flavor Type:

Sweet   Tart/Sour   Herbal   Bitter   Spicy

Flavor Strength:

Too Weak   Just Right   Too Strong

Notes: Date: ___/___/___

Caffeine: Y N

SODA CHARACTERISTICS	SCORE
Bottle Shape, Style, & Color	
Labeling Aesthetics & Description	
Aroma & Drink Color	
Carbonation / Fizziness	
Drinkability / Refreshment	
Tastes as Advertised & Expected	
Overall Flavor	
Aftertaste / Finish	
Memorability	
Value for Price	
BOTTLECAP SCORE	

Brand: _____

Flavor: _____

Flavor Type:

Sweet   Tart/Sour   Herbal   Bitter   Spicy

Flavor Strength:

Too Weak   Just Right   Too Strong

Notes: Date: ___/___/___

                  Caffeine: Y N

SODA CHARACTERISTICS	SCORE
Bottle Shape, Style, & Color	
Labeling Aesthetics & Description	
Aroma & Drink Color	
Carbonation / Fizziness	
Drinkability / Refreshment	
Tastes as Advertised & Expected	
Overall Flavor	
Aftertaste / Finish	
Memorability	
Value for Price	
BOTTLECAP SCORE	

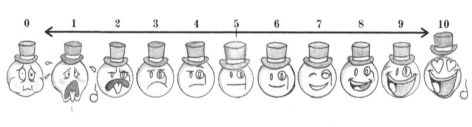

0   1   2   3   4   5   6   7   8   9   10

Brand: _____

Flavor: _____

Flavor Type:

Sweet   Tart/Sour   Herbal   Bitter   Spicy

Flavor Strength:

Too Weak   Just Right   Too Strong

Notes: Date: ___/___/___

                  Caffeine: Y N

SODA CHARACTERISTICS	SCORE
Bottle Shape, Style, & Color	
Labeling Aesthetics & Description	
Aroma & Drink Color	
Carbonation / Fizziness	
Drinkability / Refreshment	
Tastes as Advertised & Expected	
Overall Flavor	
Aftertaste / Finish	
Memorability	
Value for Price	
BOTTLECAP SCORE	

Brand: _____

Flavor: _____

Flavor Type:

Sweet   Tart/Sour   Herbal   Bitter   Spicy

Flavor Strength:

Too Weak   Just Right   Too Strong

Notes: Date: ___/___/___

          Caffeine: Y   N

SODA CHARACTERISTICS	SCORE
Bottle Shape, Style, & Color	
Labeling Aesthetics & Description	
Aroma & Drink Color	
Carbonation / Fizziness	
Drinkability / Refreshment	
Tastes as Advertised & Expected	
Overall Flavor	
Aftertaste / Finish	
Memorability	
Value for Price	
BOTTLECAP SCORE	

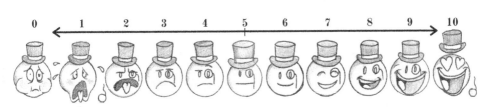

0   1   2   3   4   5   6   7   8   9   10

Brand: _____

Flavor: _____

Flavor Type:

Sweet   Tart/Sour   Herbal   Bitter   Spicy

Flavor Strength:

Too Weak   Just Right   Too Strong

Notes: Date: ___/___/___

          Caffeine: Y   N

SODA CHARACTERISTICS	SCORE
Bottle Shape, Style, & Color	
Labeling Aesthetics & Description	
Aroma & Drink Color	
Carbonation / Fizziness	
Drinkability / Refreshment	
Tastes as Advertised & Expected	
Overall Flavor	
Aftertaste / Finish	
Memorability	
Value for Price	
BOTTLECAP SCORE	

GINGER ALE & GINGER BEER FLAVORS

Brand: _____
Flavor: _____

Flavor Type:

Sweet   Tart/Sour   Herbal   Bitter   Spicy

Flavor Strength:

Too Weak   Just Right   Too Strong

Notes: Date: ___/___/___
                Caffeine: Y N

SODA CHARACTERISTICS	SCORE
Bottle Shape, Style, & Color	
Labeling Aesthetics & Description	
Aroma & Drink Color	
Carbonation / Fizziness	
Drinkability / Refreshment	
Tastes as Advertised & Expected	
Overall Flavor	
Aftertaste / Finish	
Memorability	
Value for Price	
BOTTLECAP SCORE	

Brand: _____
Flavor: _____

Flavor Type:

Sweet   Tart/Sour   Herbal   Bitter   Spicy

Flavor Strength:

Too Weak   Just Right   Too Strong

Notes: Date: ___/___/___
                Caffeine: Y N

SODA CHARACTERISTICS	SCORE
Bottle Shape, Style, & Color	
Labeling Aesthetics & Description	
Aroma & Drink Color	
Carbonation / Fizziness	
Drinkability / Refreshment	
Tastes as Advertised & Expected	
Overall Flavor	
Aftertaste / Finish	
Memorability	
Value for Price	
BOTTLECAP SCORE	

Brand: _____

Flavor: _____

Flavor Type:				
Sweet	Tart/Sour	Herbal	Bitter	Spicy

Flavor Strength:

Too Weak — Just Right — Too Strong

Notes:

Date: ___/___/___

Caffeine: Y N

SODA CHARACTERISTICS	SCORE
Bottle Shape, Style, & Color	
Labeling Aesthetics & Description	
Aroma & Drink Color	
Carbonation / Fizziness	
Drinkability / Refreshment	
Tastes as Advertised & Expected	
Overall Flavor	
Aftertaste / Finish	
Memorability	
Value for Price	
BOTTLECAP SCORE	

0 1 2 3 4 5 6 7 8 9 10

Brand: _____

Flavor: _____

Flavor Type:				
Sweet	Tart/Sour	Herbal	Bitter	Spicy

Flavor Strength:

Too Weak — Just Right — Too Strong

Notes:

Date: ___/___/___

Caffeine: Y N

SODA CHARACTERISTICS	SCORE
Bottle Shape, Style, & Color	
Labeling Aesthetics & Description	
Aroma & Drink Color	
Carbonation / Fizziness	
Drinkability / Refreshment	
Tastes as Advertised & Expected	
Overall Flavor	
Aftertaste / Finish	
Memorability	
Value for Price	
BOTTLECAP SCORE	

Brand: _____

Flavor: _____

Flavor Type:

Sweet   Tart/Sour   Herbal   Bitter   Spicy

Flavor Strength:

Too Weak   Just Right   Too Strong

Notes: Date: ___/___/___

Caffeine: Y N

SODA CHARACTERISTICS	SCORE
Bottle Shape, Style, & Color	
Labeling Aesthetics & Description	
Aroma & Drink Color	
Carbonation / Fizziness	
Drinkability / Refreshment	
Tastes as Advertised & Expected	
Overall Flavor	
Aftertaste / Finish	
Memorability	
Value for Price	
BOTTLECAP SCORE	

0   1   2   3   4   5   6   7   8   9   10

Brand: _____

Flavor: _____

Flavor Type:

Sweet   Tart/Sour   Herbal   Bitter   Spicy

Flavor Strength:

Too Weak   Just Right   Too Strong

Notes: Date: ___/___/___

Caffeine: Y N

SODA CHARACTERISTICS	SCORE
Bottle Shape, Style, & Color	
Labeling Aesthetics & Description	
Aroma & Drink Color	
Carbonation / Fizziness	
Drinkability / Refreshment	
Tastes as Advertised & Expected	
Overall Flavor	
Aftertaste / Finish	
Memorability	
Value for Price	
BOTTLECAP SCORE	

GINGER ALE & GINGER BEER FLAVORS

Brand: _____

Flavor: _____

Flavor Type:				
Sweet	Tart/Sour	Herbal	Bitter	Spicy

Flavor Strength:

Too Weak   Just Right   Too Strong

Notes: Date: ___/___/___

Caffeine: Y N

SODA CHARACTERISTICS	SCORE
Bottle Shape, Style, & Color	
Labeling Aesthetics & Description	
Aroma & Drink Color	
Carbonation / Fizziness	
Drinkability / Refreshment	
Tastes as Advertised & Expected	
Overall Flavor	
Aftertaste / Finish	
Memorability	
Value for Price	
BOTTLECAP SCORE	

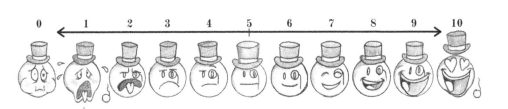

Brand: _____

Flavor: _____

Flavor Type:				
Sweet	Tart/Sour	Herbal	Bitter	Spicy

Flavor Strength:

Too Weak   Just Right   Too Strong

Notes: Date: ___/___/___

Caffeine: Y N

SODA CHARACTERISTICS	SCORE
Bottle Shape, Style, & Color	
Labeling Aesthetics & Description	
Aroma & Drink Color	
Carbonation / Fizziness	
Drinkability / Refreshment	
Tastes as Advertised & Expected	
Overall Flavor	
Aftertaste / Finish	
Memorability	
Value for Price	
BOTTLECAP SCORE	

149

Brand: _____

Flavor: _____

Flavor Type:				
Sweet	Tart/Sour	Herbal	Bitter	Spicy

Flavor Strength:

Too Weak — Just Right — Too Strong

Notes:

Date: ___/___/___

Caffeine: Y N

SODA CHARACTERISTICS	SCORE
Bottle Shape, Style, & Color	
Labeling Aesthetics & Description	
Aroma & Drink Color	
Carbonation / Fizziness	
Drinkability / Refreshment	
Tastes as Advertised & Expected	
Overall Flavor	
Aftertaste / Finish	
Memorability	
Value for Price	
BOTTLECAP SCORE	

0 1 2 3 4 5 6 7 8 9 10

Brand: _____

Flavor: _____

Flavor Type:				
Sweet	Tart/Sour	Herbal	Bitter	Spicy

Flavor Strength:

Too Weak — Just Right — Too Strong

Notes:

Date: ___/___/___

Caffeine: Y N

SODA CHARACTERISTICS	SCORE
Bottle Shape, Style, & Color	
Labeling Aesthetics & Description	
Aroma & Drink Color	
Carbonation / Fizziness	
Drinkability / Refreshment	
Tastes as Advertised & Expected	
Overall Flavor	
Aftertaste / Finish	
Memorability	
Value for Price	
BOTTLECAP SCORE	

Brand: _____

Flavor: _____

Flavor Type:

Sweet   Tart/Sour   Herbal   Bitter   Spicy

Flavor Strength:

Too Weak   Just Right   Too Strong

Notes: Date: ___/___/___

                  Caffeine: Y   N

SODA CHARACTERISTICS	SCORE
Bottle Shape, Style, & Color	
Labeling Aesthetics & Description	
Aroma & Drink Color	
Carbonation / Fizziness	
Drinkability / Refreshment	
Tastes as Advertised & Expected	
Overall Flavor	
Aftertaste / Finish	
Memorability	
Value for Price	
BOTTLECAP SCORE	

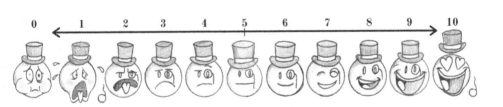

0   1   2   3   4   5   6   7   8   9   10

Brand: _____

Flavor: _____

Flavor Type:

Sweet   Tart/Sour   Herbal   Bitter   Spicy

Flavor Strength:

Too Weak   Just Right   Too Strong

Notes: Date: ___/___/___

                  Caffeine: Y   N

SODA CHARACTERISTICS	SCORE
Bottle Shape, Style, & Color	
Labeling Aesthetics & Description	
Aroma & Drink Color	
Carbonation / Fizziness	
Drinkability / Refreshment	
Tastes as Advertised & Expected	
Overall Flavor	
Aftertaste / Finish	
Memorability	
Value for Price	
BOTTLECAP SCORE	

GRAPE FLAVORS

Brand	Flavor	Score	Notes	Page
				153
				153
				154
				154
				155
				155
				156
				156
				157
				157
				158
				158
				159
				159
				160
				160
				161
				161
				162
				162
				163
				163
				164
				164
				165
				165

Brand: _____

Flavor: _____

Flavor Type:

Sweet   Tart/Sour   Herbal   Bitter   Spicy

Flavor Strength:

|———————|———————|———————|
Too Weak   Just Right   Too Strong

Notes: Date: ___/___/___

                Caffeine: Y   N

SODA CHARACTERISTICS	SCORE
Bottle Shape, Style, & Color	
Labeling Aesthetics & Description	
Aroma & Drink Color	
Carbonation / Fizziness	
Drinkability / Refreshment	
Tastes as Advertised & Expected	
Overall Flavor	
Aftertaste / Finish	
Memorability	
Value for Price	
BOTTLECAP SCORE	

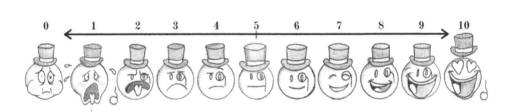

Brand: _____

Flavor: _____

Flavor Type:

Sweet   Tart/Sour   Herbal   Bitter   Spicy

Flavor Strength:

|———————|———————|———————|
Too Weak   Just Right   Too Strong

Notes: Date: ___/___/___

                Caffeine: Y   N

SODA CHARACTERISTICS	SCORE
Bottle Shape, Style, & Color	
Labeling Aesthetics & Description	
Aroma & Drink Color	
Carbonation / Fizziness	
Drinkability / Refreshment	
Tastes as Advertised & Expected	
Overall Flavor	
Aftertaste / Finish	
Memorability	
Value for Price	
BOTTLECAP SCORE	

Brand: _____

Flavor: _____

| Flavor Type: |
| Sweet   Tart/Sour   Herbal   Bitter   Spicy |

| Flavor Strength: |
| Too Weak   Just Right   Too Strong |

Notes: Date: ___/___/___

Caffeine: Y   N

SODA CHARACTERISTICS	SCORE
Bottle Shape, Style, & Color	
Labeling Aesthetics & Description	
Aroma & Drink Color	
Carbonation / Fizziness	
Drinkability / Refreshment	
Tastes as Advertised & Expected	
Overall Flavor	
Aftertaste / Finish	
Memorability	
Value for Price	
BOTTLECAP SCORE	

0   1   2   3   4   5   6   7   8   9   10

Brand: _____

Flavor: _____

| Flavor Type: |
| Sweet   Tart/Sour   Herbal   Bitter   Spicy |

| Flavor Strength: |
| Too Weak   Just Right   Too Strong |

Notes: Date: ___/___/___

Caffeine: Y   N

SODA CHARACTERISTICS	SCORE
Bottle Shape, Style, & Color	
Labeling Aesthetics & Description	
Aroma & Drink Color	
Carbonation / Fizziness	
Drinkability / Refreshment	
Tastes as Advertised & Expected	
Overall Flavor	
Aftertaste / Finish	
Memorability	
Value for Price	
BOTTLECAP SCORE	

Brand: _____

Flavor: _____

Flavor Type:				
Sweet	Tart/Sour	Herbal	Bitter	Spicy

Flavor Strength:

Too Weak   Just Right   Too Strong

Notes: Date: ___/___/___

Caffeine: Y N

SODA CHARACTERISTICS	SCORE
Bottle Shape, Style, & Color	
Labeling Aesthetics & Description	
Aroma & Drink Color	
Carbonation / Fizziness	
Drinkability / Refreshment	
Tastes as Advertised & Expected	
Overall Flavor	
Aftertaste / Finish	
Memorability	
Value for Price	
BOTTLECAP SCORE	

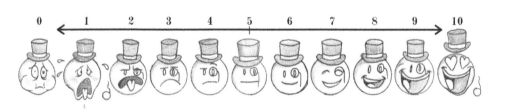

Brand: _____

Flavor: _____

Flavor Type:				
Sweet	Tart/Sour	Herbal	Bitter	Spicy

Flavor Strength:

Too Weak   Just Right   Too Strong

Notes: Date: ___/___/___

Caffeine: Y N

SODA CHARACTERISTICS	SCORE
Bottle Shape, Style, & Color	
Labeling Aesthetics & Description	
Aroma & Drink Color	
Carbonation / Fizziness	
Drinkability / Refreshment	
Tastes as Advertised & Expected	
Overall Flavor	
Aftertaste / Finish	
Memorability	
Value for Price	
BOTTLECAP SCORE	

Brand: _____

Flavor: _____

Flavor Type:				
Sweet	Tart/Sour	Herbal	Bitter	Spicy

Flavor Strength:

Too Weak ——— Just Right ——— Too Strong

Notes:

Date: ___/___/___

Caffeine: Y N

SODA CHARACTERISTICS	SCORE
Bottle Shape, Style, & Color	
Labeling Aesthetics & Description	
Aroma & Drink Color	
Carbonation / Fizziness	
Drinkability / Refreshment	
Tastes as Advertised & Expected	
Overall Flavor	
Aftertaste / Finish	
Memorability	
Value for Price	
BOTTLECAP SCORE	

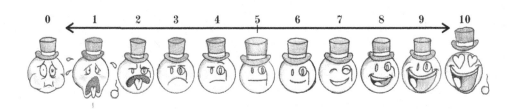

Brand: _____

Flavor: _____

Flavor Type:				
Sweet	Tart/Sour	Herbal	Bitter	Spicy

Flavor Strength:

Too Weak ——— Just Right ——— Too Strong

Notes:

Date: ___/___/___

Caffeine: Y N

SODA CHARACTERISTICS	SCORE
Bottle Shape, Style, & Color	
Labeling Aesthetics & Description	
Aroma & Drink Color	
Carbonation / Fizziness	
Drinkability / Refreshment	
Tastes as Advertised & Expected	
Overall Flavor	
Aftertaste / Finish	
Memorability	
Value for Price	
BOTTLECAP SCORE	

Brand: _____

Flavor: _____

Flavor Type:

Sweet   Tart/Sour   Herbal   Bitter   Spicy

Flavor Strength:

Too Weak   Just Right   Too Strong

Notes: Date: ___/___/___

Caffeine: Y   N

SODA CHARACTERISTICS	SCORE
Bottle Shape, Style, & Color	
Labeling Aesthetics & Description	
Aroma & Drink Color	
Carbonation / Fizziness	
Drinkability / Refreshment	
Tastes as Advertised & Expected	
Overall Flavor	
Aftertaste / Finish	
Memorability	
Value for Price	
BOTTLECAP SCORE	

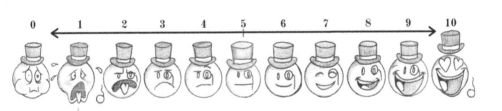

0   1   2   3   4   5   6   7   8   9   10

Brand: _____

Flavor: _____

Flavor Type:

Sweet   Tart/Sour   Herbal   Bitter   Spicy

Flavor Strength:

Too Weak   Just Right   Too Strong

Notes: Date: ___/___/___

Caffeine: Y   N

SODA CHARACTERISTICS	SCORE
Bottle Shape, Style, & Color	
Labeling Aesthetics & Description	
Aroma & Drink Color	
Carbonation / Fizziness	
Drinkability / Refreshment	
Tastes as Advertised & Expected	
Overall Flavor	
Aftertaste / Finish	
Memorability	
Value for Price	
BOTTLECAP SCORE	

Brand: _____

Flavor: _____

Flavor Type:

Sweet   Tart/Sour   Herbal   Bitter   Spicy

Flavor Strength:

Too Weak   Just Right   Too Strong

Notes: Date: ___/___/___

Caffeine: Y N

SODA CHARACTERISTICS	SCORE
Bottle Shape, Style, & Color	
Labeling Aesthetics & Description	
Aroma & Drink Color	
Carbonation / Fizziness	
Drinkability / Refreshment	
Tastes as Advertised & Expected	
Overall Flavor	
Aftertaste / Finish	
Memorability	
Value for Price	
BOTTLECAP SCORE	

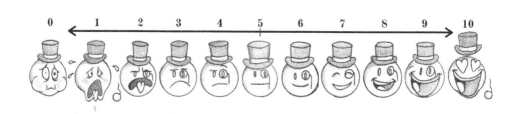

| 0 | 1 | 2 | 3 | 4 | 5 | 6 | 7 | 8 | 9 | 10 |

Brand: _____

Flavor: _____

Flavor Type:

Sweet   Tart/Sour   Herbal   Bitter   Spicy

Flavor Strength:

Too Weak   Just Right   Too Strong

Notes: Date: ___/___/___

Caffeine: Y N

SODA CHARACTERISTICS	SCORE
Bottle Shape, Style, & Color	
Labeling Aesthetics & Description	
Aroma & Drink Color	
Carbonation / Fizziness	
Drinkability / Refreshment	
Tastes as Advertised & Expected	
Overall Flavor	
Aftertaste / Finish	
Memorability	
Value for Price	
BOTTLECAP SCORE	

Brand: _____

Flavor: _____

Flavor Type:

Sweet   Tart/Sour   Herbal   Bitter   Spicy

Flavor Strength:

Too Weak   Just Right   Too Strong

Notes: Date: ___/___/___

Caffeine: Y N

SODA CHARACTERISTICS	SCORE
Bottle Shape, Style, & Color	
Labeling Aesthetics & Description	
Aroma & Drink Color	
Carbonation / Fizziness	
Drinkability / Refreshment	
Tastes as Advertised & Expected	
Overall Flavor	
Aftertaste / Finish	
Memorability	
Value for Price	
BOTTLECAP SCORE	

Brand: _____

Flavor: _____

Flavor Type:

Sweet   Tart/Sour   Herbal   Bitter   Spicy

Flavor Strength:

Too Weak   Just Right   Too Strong

Notes: Date: ___/___/___

Caffeine: Y N

SODA CHARACTERISTICS	SCORE
Bottle Shape, Style, & Color	
Labeling Aesthetics & Description	
Aroma & Drink Color	
Carbonation / Fizziness	
Drinkability / Refreshment	
Tastes as Advertised & Expected	
Overall Flavor	
Aftertaste / Finish	
Memorability	
Value for Price	
BOTTLECAP SCORE	

159

Brand: _____

Flavor: _____

Flavor Type:

Sweet   Tart/Sour   Herbal   Bitter   Spicy

Flavor Strength:

Too Weak   Just Right   Too Strong

Notes: Date: ___/___/___

                Caffeine: Y N

SODA CHARACTERISTICS	SCORE
Bottle Shape, Style, & Color	
Labeling Aesthetics & Description	
Aroma & Drink Color	
Carbonation / Fizziness	
Drinkability / Refreshment	
Tastes as Advertised & Expected	
Overall Flavor	
Aftertaste / Finish	
Memorability	
Value for Price	
BOTTLECAP SCORE	

0   1   2   3   4   5   6   7   8   9   10

Brand: _____

Flavor: _____

Flavor Type:

Sweet   Tart/Sour   Herbal   Bitter   Spicy

Flavor Strength:

Too Weak   Just Right   Too Strong

Notes: Date: ___/___/___

                Caffeine: Y N

SODA CHARACTERISTICS	SCORE
Bottle Shape, Style, & Color	
Labeling Aesthetics & Description	
Aroma & Drink Color	
Carbonation / Fizziness	
Drinkability / Refreshment	
Tastes as Advertised & Expected	
Overall Flavor	
Aftertaste / Finish	
Memorability	
Value for Price	
BOTTLECAP SCORE	

Brand: _____

Flavor: _____

Flavor Type:

Sweet   Tart/Sour   Herbal   Bitter   Spicy

Flavor Strength:

Too Weak   Just Right   Too Strong

Notes: Date: ___/___/___

Caffeine: Y   N

SODA CHARACTERISTICS	SCORE
Bottle Shape, Style, & Color	
Labeling Aesthetics & Description	
Aroma & Drink Color	
Carbonation / Fizziness	
Drinkability / Refreshment	
Tastes as Advertised & Expected	
Overall Flavor	
Aftertaste / Finish	
Memorability	
Value for Price	
BOTTLECAP SCORE	

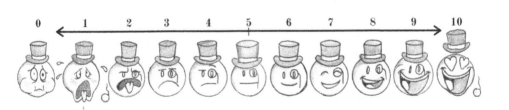

0   1   2   3   4   5   6   7   8   9   10

Brand: _____

Flavor: _____

Flavor Type:

Sweet   Tart/Sour   Herbal   Bitter   Spicy

Flavor Strength:

Too Weak   Just Right   Too Strong

Notes: Date: ___/___/___

Caffeine: Y   N

SODA CHARACTERISTICS	SCORE
Bottle Shape, Style, & Color	
Labeling Aesthetics & Description	
Aroma & Drink Color	
Carbonation / Fizziness	
Drinkability / Refreshment	
Tastes as Advertised & Expected	
Overall Flavor	
Aftertaste / Finish	
Memorability	
Value for Price	
BOTTLECAP SCORE	

Brand: _____

Flavor: _____

Flavor Type:

Sweet   Tart/Sour   Herbal   Bitter   Spicy

Flavor Strength:

Too Weak   Just Right   Too Strong

Notes: Date: ___/___/___

Caffeine: Y N

SODA CHARACTERISTICS	SCORE
Bottle Shape, Style, & Color	
Labeling Aesthetics & Description	
Aroma & Drink Color	
Carbonation / Fizziness	
Drinkability / Refreshment	
Tastes as Advertised & Expected	
Overall Flavor	
Aftertaste / Finish	
Memorability	
Value for Price	
BOTTLECAP SCORE	

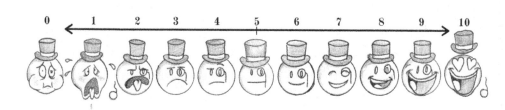

0   1   2   3   4   5   6   7   8   9   10

Brand: _____

Flavor: _____

Flavor Type:

Sweet   Tart/Sour   Herbal   Bitter   Spicy

Flavor Strength:

Too Weak   Just Right   Too Strong

Notes: Date: ___/___/___

Caffeine: Y N

SODA CHARACTERISTICS	SCORE
Bottle Shape, Style, & Color	
Labeling Aesthetics & Description	
Aroma & Drink Color	
Carbonation / Fizziness	
Drinkability / Refreshment	
Tastes as Advertised & Expected	
Overall Flavor	
Aftertaste / Finish	
Memorability	
Value for Price	
BOTTLECAP SCORE	

Brand: _____

Flavor: _____

Flavor Type:

Sweet   Tart/Sour   Herbal   Bitter   Spicy

Flavor Strength:

Too Weak   Just Right   Too Strong

Notes: Date: ___/___/___

Caffeine: Y   N

SODA CHARACTERISTICS	SCORE
Bottle Shape, Style, & Color	
Labeling Aesthetics & Description	
Aroma & Drink Color	
Carbonation / Fizziness	
Drinkability / Refreshment	
Tastes as Advertised & Expected	
Overall Flavor	
Aftertaste / Finish	
Memorability	
Value for Price	
BOTTLECAP SCORE	

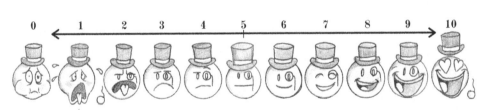

0   1   2   3   4   5   6   7   8   9   10

Brand: _____

Flavor: _____

Flavor Type:

Sweet   Tart/Sour   Herbal   Bitter   Spicy

Flavor Strength:

Too Weak   Just Right   Too Strong

Notes: Date: ___/___/___

Caffeine: Y   N

SODA CHARACTERISTICS	SCORE
Bottle Shape, Style, & Color	
Labeling Aesthetics & Description	
Aroma & Drink Color	
Carbonation / Fizziness	
Drinkability / Refreshment	
Tastes as Advertised & Expected	
Overall Flavor	
Aftertaste / Finish	
Memorability	
Value for Price	
BOTTLECAP SCORE	

Brand: _____

Flavor: _____

SODA CHARACTERISTICS	SCORE
Bottle Shape, Style, & Color	
Labeling Aesthetics & Description	
Aroma & Drink Color	
Carbonation / Fizziness	
Drinkability / Refreshment	
Tastes as Advertised & Expected	
Overall Flavor	
Aftertaste / Finish	
Memorability	
Value for Price	
BOTTLECAP SCORE	

Flavor Type:

Sweet   Tart/Sour   Herbal   Bitter   Spicy

Flavor Strength:

Too Weak   Just Right   Too Strong

Notes: Date: ___/___/___

Caffeine: Y   N

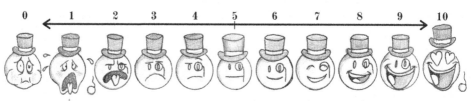

Brand: _____

Flavor: _____

SODA CHARACTERISTICS	SCORE
Bottle Shape, Style, & Color	
Labeling Aesthetics & Description	
Aroma & Drink Color	
Carbonation / Fizziness	
Drinkability / Refreshment	
Tastes as Advertised & Expected	
Overall Flavor	
Aftertaste / Finish	
Memorability	
Value for Price	
BOTTLECAP SCORE	

Flavor Type:

Sweet   Tart/Sour   Herbal   Bitter   Spicy

Flavor Strength:

Too Weak   Just Right   Too Strong

Notes: Date: ___/___/___

Caffeine: Y   N

Brand: _____

Flavor: _____

Flavor Type:				
Sweet	Tart/Sour	Herbal	Bitter	Spicy

Flavor Strength:

Too Weak   Just Right   Too Strong

Notes: Date: ___/___/___

Caffeine: Y N

SODA CHARACTERISTICS	SCORE
Bottle Shape, Style, & Color	
Labeling Aesthetics & Description	
Aroma & Drink Color	
Carbonation / Fizziness	
Drinkability / Refreshment	
Tastes as Advertised & Expected	
Overall Flavor	
Aftertaste / Finish	
Memorability	
Value for Price	
BOTTLECAP SCORE	

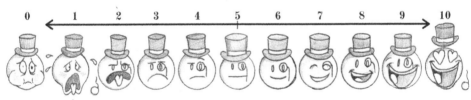

Brand: _____

Flavor: _____

Flavor Type:				
Sweet	Tart/Sour	Herbal	Bitter	Spicy

Flavor Strength:

Too Weak   Just Right   Too Strong

Notes: Date: ___/___/___

Caffeine: Y N

SODA CHARACTERISTICS	SCORE
Bottle Shape, Style, & Color	
Labeling Aesthetics & Description	
Aroma & Drink Color	
Carbonation / Fizziness	
Drinkability / Refreshment	
Tastes as Advertised & Expected	
Overall Flavor	
Aftertaste / Finish	
Memorability	
Value for Price	
BOTTLECAP SCORE	

LEMON & LIME FLAVORS

Brand	Flavor	Score	Notes	Page
				167
				167
				168
				168
				169
				169
				170
				170
				171
				171
				172
				172
				173
				173
				174
				174
				175
				175
				176
				176
				177
				177
				178
				178
				179
				179

LEMON & LIME FLAVORS

Brand: _____

Flavor: _____

Flavor Type:

Sweet   Tart/Sour   Herbal   Bitter   Spicy

Flavor Strength:

Too Weak   Just Right   Too Strong

Notes: Date: ___/___/___

Caffeine: Y N

SODA CHARACTERISTICS	SCORE
Bottle Shape, Style, & Color	
Labeling Aesthetics & Description	
Aroma & Drink Color	
Carbonation / Fizziness	
Drinkability / Refreshment	
Tastes as Advertised & Expected	
Overall Flavor	
Aftertaste / Finish	
Memorability	
Value for Price	
BOTTLECAP SCORE	

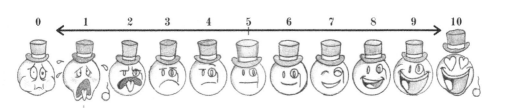

0   1   2   3   4   5   6   7   8   9   10

Brand: _____

Flavor: _____

Flavor Type:

Sweet   Tart/Sour   Herbal   Bitter   Spicy

Flavor Strength:

Too Weak   Just Right   Too Strong

Notes: Date: ___/___/___

Caffeine: Y N

SODA CHARACTERISTICS	SCORE
Bottle Shape, Style, & Color	
Labeling Aesthetics & Description	
Aroma & Drink Color	
Carbonation / Fizziness	
Drinkability / Refreshment	
Tastes as Advertised & Expected	
Overall Flavor	
Aftertaste / Finish	
Memorability	
Value for Price	
BOTTLECAP SCORE	

Brand: _____

Flavor: _____

SODA CHARACTERISTICS	SCORE
Bottle Shape, Style, & Color	
Labeling Aesthetics & Description	
Aroma & Drink Color	
Carbonation / Fizziness	
Drinkability / Refreshment	
Tastes as Advertised & Expected	
Overall Flavor	
Aftertaste / Finish	
Memorability	
Value for Price	
BOTTLECAP SCORE	

Flavor Type:

Sweet   Tart/Sour   Herbal   Bitter   Spicy

Flavor Strength:

Too Weak   Just Right   Too Strong

Notes: Date: ___/___/___

Caffeine: Y   N

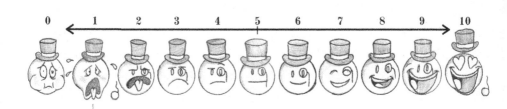

Brand: _____

Flavor: _____

SODA CHARACTERISTICS	SCORE
Bottle Shape, Style, & Color	
Labeling Aesthetics & Description	
Aroma & Drink Color	
Carbonation / Fizziness	
Drinkability / Refreshment	
Tastes as Advertised & Expected	
Overall Flavor	
Aftertaste / Finish	
Memorability	
Value for Price	
BOTTLECAP SCORE	

Flavor Type:

Sweet   Tart/Sour   Herbal   Bitter   Spicy

Flavor Strength:

Too Weak   Just Right   Too Strong

Notes: Date: ___/___/___

Caffeine: Y   N

LEMON & LIME FLAVORS

Brand: _____

Flavor: _____

Flavor Type:

Sweet   Tart/Sour   Herbal   Bitter   Spicy

Flavor Strength:

Too Weak   Just Right   Too Strong

Notes: Date: ___/___/___

                Caffeine: Y N

SODA CHARACTERISTICS	SCORE
Bottle Shape, Style, & Color	
Labeling Aesthetics & Description	
Aroma & Drink Color	
Carbonation / Fizziness	
Drinkability / Refreshment	
Tastes as Advertised & Expected	
Overall Flavor	
Aftertaste / Finish	
Memorability	
Value for Price	
BOTTLECAP SCORE	

0   1   2   3   4   5   6   7   8   9   10

Brand: _____

Flavor: _____

Flavor Type:

Sweet   Tart/Sour   Herbal   Bitter   Spicy

Flavor Strength:

Too Weak   Just Right   Too Strong

Notes: Date: ___/___/___

                Caffeine: Y N

SODA CHARACTERISTICS	SCORE
Bottle Shape, Style, & Color	
Labeling Aesthetics & Description	
Aroma & Drink Color	
Carbonation / Fizziness	
Drinkability / Refreshment	
Tastes as Advertised & Expected	
Overall Flavor	
Aftertaste / Finish	
Memorability	
Value for Price	
BOTTLECAP SCORE	

Brand: _____

Flavor: _____

Flavor Type:

Sweet   Tart/Sour   Herbal   Bitter   Spicy

Flavor Strength:

Too Weak   Just Right   Too Strong

Notes: Date: ___/___/___

Caffeine: Y N

SODA CHARACTERISTICS	SCORE
Bottle Shape, Style, & Color	
Labeling Aesthetics & Description	
Aroma & Drink Color	
Carbonation / Fizziness	
Drinkability / Refreshment	
Tastes as Advertised & Expected	
Overall Flavor	
Aftertaste / Finish	
Memorability	
Value for Price	
BOTTLECAP SCORE	

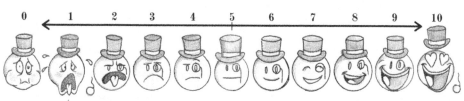

0   1   2   3   4   5   6   7   8   9   10

Brand: _____

Flavor: _____

Flavor Type:

Sweet   Tart/Sour   Herbal   Bitter   Spicy

Flavor Strength:

Too Weak   Just Right   Too Strong

Notes: Date: ___/___/___

Caffeine: Y N

SODA CHARACTERISTICS	SCORE
Bottle Shape, Style, & Color	
Labeling Aesthetics & Description	
Aroma & Drink Color	
Carbonation / Fizziness	
Drinkability / Refreshment	
Tastes as Advertised & Expected	
Overall Flavor	
Aftertaste / Finish	
Memorability	
Value for Price	
BOTTLECAP SCORE	

Brand: _____

Flavor: _____

Flavor Type:

Sweet   Tart/Sour   Herbal   Bitter   Spicy

Flavor Strength:

Too Weak   Just Right   Too Strong

Notes: Date: ___/___/___

              Caffeine: Y   N

SODA CHARACTERISTICS	SCORE
Bottle Shape, Style, & Color	
Labeling Aesthetics & Description	
Aroma & Drink Color	
Carbonation / Fizziness	
Drinkability / Refreshment	
Tastes as Advertised & Expected	
Overall Flavor	
Aftertaste / Finish	
Memorability	
Value for Price	
BOTTLECAP SCORE	

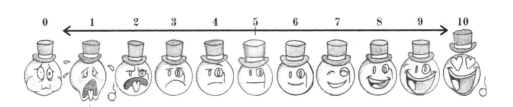

0   1   2   3   4   5   6   7   8   9   10

Brand: _____

Flavor: _____

Flavor Type:

Sweet   Tart/Sour   Herbal   Bitter   Spicy

Flavor Strength:

Too Weak   Just Right   Too Strong

Notes: Date: ___/___/___

              Caffeine: Y   N

SODA CHARACTERISTICS	SCORE
Bottle Shape, Style, & Color	
Labeling Aesthetics & Description	
Aroma & Drink Color	
Carbonation / Fizziness	
Drinkability / Refreshment	
Tastes as Advertised & Expected	
Overall Flavor	
Aftertaste / Finish	
Memorability	
Value for Price	
BOTTLECAP SCORE	

Brand: _____

Flavor: _____

Flavor Type:

Sweet   Tart/Sour   Herbal   Bitter   Spicy

Flavor Strength:

Too Weak   Just Right   Too Strong

Notes: Date: ___/___/___

Caffeine: Y N

SODA CHARACTERISTICS	SCORE
Bottle Shape, Style, & Color	
Labeling Aesthetics & Description	
Aroma & Drink Color	
Carbonation / Fizziness	
Drinkability / Refreshment	
Tastes as Advertised & Expected	
Overall Flavor	
Aftertaste / Finish	
Memorability	
Value for Price	
BOTTLECAP SCORE	

0   1   2   3   4   5   6   7   8   9   10

Brand: _____

Flavor: _____

Flavor Type:

Sweet   Tart/Sour   Herbal   Bitter   Spicy

Flavor Strength:

Too Weak   Just Right   Too Strong

Notes: Date: ___/___/___

Caffeine: Y N

SODA CHARACTERISTICS	SCORE
Bottle Shape, Style, & Color	
Labeling Aesthetics & Description	
Aroma & Drink Color	
Carbonation / Fizziness	
Drinkability / Refreshment	
Tastes as Advertised & Expected	
Overall Flavor	
Aftertaste / Finish	
Memorability	
Value for Price	
BOTTLECAP SCORE	

Brand: _____

Flavor: _____

Flavor Type:				
Sweet	Tart/Sour	Herbal	Bitter	Spicy

Flavor Strength:

Too Weak   Just Right   Too Strong

Notes: Date: ___/___/___

Caffeine: Y N

SODA CHARACTERISTICS	SCORE
Bottle Shape, Style, & Color	
Labeling Aesthetics & Description	
Aroma & Drink Color	
Carbonation / Fizziness	
Drinkability / Refreshment	
Tastes as Advertised & Expected	
Overall Flavor	
Aftertaste / Finish	
Memorability	
Value for Price	
BOTTLECAP SCORE	

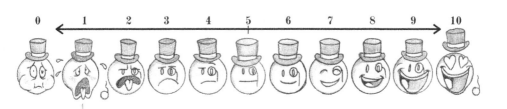

0   1   2   3   4   5   6   7   8   9   10

Brand: _____

Flavor: _____

Flavor Type:				
Sweet	Tart/Sour	Herbal	Bitter	Spicy

Flavor Strength:

Too Weak   Just Right   Too Strong

Notes: Date: ___/___/___

Caffeine: Y N

SODA CHARACTERISTICS	SCORE
Bottle Shape, Style, & Color	
Labeling Aesthetics & Description	
Aroma & Drink Color	
Carbonation / Fizziness	
Drinkability / Refreshment	
Tastes as Advertised & Expected	
Overall Flavor	
Aftertaste / Finish	
Memorability	
Value for Price	
BOTTLECAP SCORE	

Brand: _____

Flavor: _____

Flavor Type:				
Sweet	Tart/Sour	Herbal	Bitter	Spicy

Flavor Strength:
Too Weak   Just Right   Too Strong

Notes: Date: ___/___/___

Caffeine: Y   N

SODA CHARACTERISTICS	SCORE
Bottle Shape, Style, & Color	
Labeling Aesthetics & Description	
Aroma & Drink Color	
Carbonation / Fizziness	
Drinkability / Refreshment	
Tastes as Advertised & Expected	
Overall Flavor	
Aftertaste / Finish	
Memorability	
Value for Price	
BOTTLECAP SCORE	

Brand: _____

Flavor: _____

Flavor Type:				
Sweet	Tart/Sour	Herbal	Bitter	Spicy

Flavor Strength:
Too Weak   Just Right   Too Strong

Notes: Date: ___/___/___

Caffeine: Y   N

SODA CHARACTERISTICS	SCORE
Bottle Shape, Style, & Color	
Labeling Aesthetics & Description	
Aroma & Drink Color	
Carbonation / Fizziness	
Drinkability / Refreshment	
Tastes as Advertised & Expected	
Overall Flavor	
Aftertaste / Finish	
Memorability	
Value for Price	
BOTTLECAP SCORE	

Brand: _____

Flavor: _____

Flavor Type:

Sweet   Tart/Sour   Herbal   Bitter   Spicy

Flavor Strength:

Too Weak   Just Right   Too Strong

Notes: Date: ___/___/___

        Caffeine: Y   N

SODA CHARACTERISTICS	SCORE
Bottle Shape, Style, & Color	
Labeling Aesthetics & Description	
Aroma & Drink Color	
Carbonation / Fizziness	
Drinkability / Refreshment	
Tastes as Advertised & Expected	
Overall Flavor	
Aftertaste / Finish	
Memorability	
Value for Price	
BOTTLECAP SCORE	

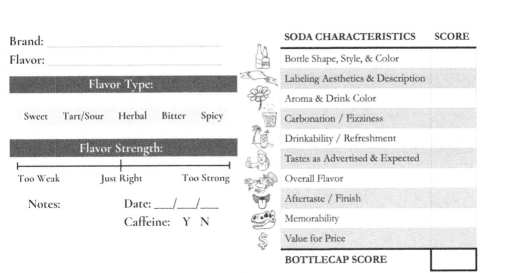

0   1   2   3   4   5   6   7   8   9   10

Brand: _____

Flavor: _____

Flavor Type:

Sweet   Tart/Sour   Herbal   Bitter   Spicy

Flavor Strength:

Too Weak   Just Right   Too Strong

Notes: Date: ___/___/___

        Caffeine: Y   N

SODA CHARACTERISTICS	SCORE
Bottle Shape, Style, & Color	
Labeling Aesthetics & Description	
Aroma & Drink Color	
Carbonation / Fizziness	
Drinkability / Refreshment	
Tastes as Advertised & Expected	
Overall Flavor	
Aftertaste / Finish	
Memorability	
Value for Price	
BOTTLECAP SCORE	

Brand: _____

Flavor: _____

Flavor Type:

Sweet   Tart/Sour   Herbal   Bitter   Spicy

Flavor Strength:

Too Weak   Just Right   Too Strong

Notes: Date: ___/___/___

Caffeine: Y   N

SODA CHARACTERISTICS	SCORE
Bottle Shape, Style, & Color	
Labeling Aesthetics & Description	
Aroma & Drink Color	
Carbonation / Fizziness	
Drinkability / Refreshment	
Tastes as Advertised & Expected	
Overall Flavor	
Aftertaste / Finish	
Memorability	
Value for Price	
BOTTLECAP SCORE	

0   1   2   3   4   5   6   7   8   9   10

Brand: _____

Flavor: _____

Flavor Type:

Sweet   Tart/Sour   Herbal   Bitter   Spicy

Flavor Strength:

Too Weak   Just Right   Too Strong

Notes: Date: ___/___/___

Caffeine: Y   N

SODA CHARACTERISTICS	SCORE
Bottle Shape, Style, & Color	
Labeling Aesthetics & Description	
Aroma & Drink Color	
Carbonation / Fizziness	
Drinkability / Refreshment	
Tastes as Advertised & Expected	
Overall Flavor	
Aftertaste / Finish	
Memorability	
Value for Price	
BOTTLECAP SCORE	

Brand: _____

Flavor: _____

Flavor Type:

Sweet   Tart/Sour   Herbal   Bitter   Spicy

Flavor Strength:

Too Weak   Just Right   Too Strong

Notes: Date: ___/___/___

Caffeine: Y N

SODA CHARACTERISTICS	SCORE
Bottle Shape, Style, & Color	
Labeling Aesthetics & Description	
Aroma & Drink Color	
Carbonation / Fizziness	
Drinkability / Refreshment	
Tastes as Advertised & Expected	
Overall Flavor	
Aftertaste / Finish	
Memorability	
Value for Price	
BOTTLECAP SCORE	

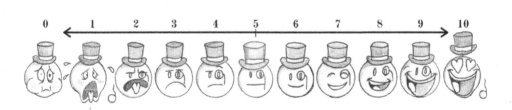

0   1   2   3   4   5   6   7   8   9   10

Brand: _____

Flavor: _____

Flavor Type:

Sweet   Tart/Sour   Herbal   Bitter   Spicy

Flavor Strength:

Too Weak   Just Right   Too Strong

Notes: Date: ___/___/___

Caffeine: Y N

SODA CHARACTERISTICS	SCORE
Bottle Shape, Style, & Color	
Labeling Aesthetics & Description	
Aroma & Drink Color	
Carbonation / Fizziness	
Drinkability / Refreshment	
Tastes as Advertised & Expected	
Overall Flavor	
Aftertaste / Finish	
Memorability	
Value for Price	
BOTTLECAP SCORE	

Brand: _____

Flavor: _____

Flavor Type:

Sweet   Tart/Sour   Herbal   Bitter   Spicy

Flavor Strength:

Too Weak   Just Right   Too Strong

Notes: Date: ___/___/___

Caffeine: Y N

SODA CHARACTERISTICS	SCORE
Bottle Shape, Style, & Color	
Labeling Aesthetics & Description	
Aroma & Drink Color	
Carbonation / Fizziness	
Drinkability / Refreshment	
Tastes as Advertised & Expected	
Overall Flavor	
Aftertaste / Finish	
Memorability	
Value for Price	
BOTTLECAP SCORE	

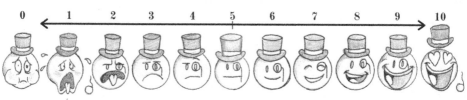

Brand: _____

Flavor: _____

Flavor Type:

Sweet   Tart/Sour   Herbal   Bitter   Spicy

Flavor Strength:

Too Weak   Just Right   Too Strong

Notes: Date: ___/___/___

Caffeine: Y N

SODA CHARACTERISTICS	SCORE
Bottle Shape, Style, & Color	
Labeling Aesthetics & Description	
Aroma & Drink Color	
Carbonation / Fizziness	
Drinkability / Refreshment	
Tastes as Advertised & Expected	
Overall Flavor	
Aftertaste / Finish	
Memorability	
Value for Price	
BOTTLECAP SCORE	

Brand: _____

Flavor: _____

Flavor Type:				
Sweet	Tart/Sour	Herbal	Bitter	Spicy

Flavor Strength:

Too Weak   Just Right   Too Strong

Notes: Date: ___/___/___

Caffeine: Y N

SODA CHARACTERISTICS	SCORE
Bottle Shape, Style, & Color	
Labeling Aesthetics & Description	
Aroma & Drink Color	
Carbonation / Fizziness	
Drinkability / Refreshment	
Tastes as Advertised & Expected	
Overall Flavor	
Aftertaste / Finish	
Memorability	
Value for Price	
BOTTLECAP SCORE	

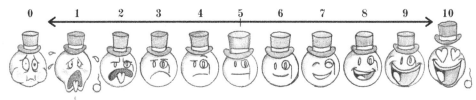

0   1   2   3   4   5   6   7   8   9   10

Brand: _____

Flavor: _____

Flavor Type:				
Sweet	Tart/Sour	Herbal	Bitter	Spicy

Flavor Strength:

Too Weak   Just Right   Too Strong

Notes: Date: ___/___/___

Caffeine: Y N

SODA CHARACTERISTICS	SCORE
Bottle Shape, Style, & Color	
Labeling Aesthetics & Description	
Aroma & Drink Color	
Carbonation / Fizziness	
Drinkability / Refreshment	
Tastes as Advertised & Expected	
Overall Flavor	
Aftertaste / Finish	
Memorability	
Value for Price	
BOTTLECAP SCORE	

ORANGE FLAVORS

Brand	Flavor	Score	Notes	Page
				181
				181
				182
				182
				183
				183
				184
				184
				185
				185
				186
				186
				187
				187
				188
				188
				189
				189
				190
				190
				191
				191
				192
				192
				193
				193

Brand: _____

Flavor: _____

Flavor Type:

Sweet   Tart/Sour   Herbal   Bitter   Spicy

Flavor Strength:

Too Weak   Just Right   Too Strong

Notes: Date: ___/___/___

Caffeine: Y   N

SODA CHARACTERISTICS	SCORE
Bottle Shape, Style, & Color	
Labeling Aesthetics & Description	
Aroma & Drink Color	
Carbonation / Fizziness	
Drinkability / Refreshment	
Tastes as Advertised & Expected	
Overall Flavor	
Aftertaste / Finish	
Memorability	
Value for Price	
BOTTLECAP SCORE	

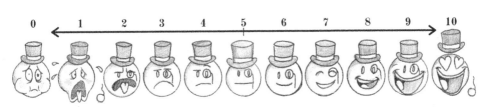

0   1   2   3   4   5   6   7   8   9   10

Brand: _____

Flavor: _____

Flavor Type:

Sweet   Tart/Sour   Herbal   Bitter   Spicy

Flavor Strength:

Too Weak   Just Right   Too Strong

Notes: Date: ___/___/___

Caffeine: Y   N

SODA CHARACTERISTICS	SCORE
Bottle Shape, Style, & Color	
Labeling Aesthetics & Description	
Aroma & Drink Color	
Carbonation / Fizziness	
Drinkability / Refreshment	
Tastes as Advertised & Expected	
Overall Flavor	
Aftertaste / Finish	
Memorability	
Value for Price	
BOTTLECAP SCORE	

Brand: _____

Flavor: _____

Flavor Type:

Sweet   Tart/Sour   Herbal   Bitter   Spicy

Flavor Strength:

├─────────────┼─────────────┤
Too Weak   Just Right   Too Strong

Notes: Date: ___/___/___

Caffeine: Y N

SODA CHARACTERISTICS	SCORE
Bottle Shape, Style, & Color	
Labeling Aesthetics & Description	
Aroma & Drink Color	
Carbonation / Fizziness	
Drinkability / Refreshment	
Tastes as Advertised & Expected	
Overall Flavor	
Aftertaste / Finish	
Memorability	
Value for Price	
BOTTLECAP SCORE	

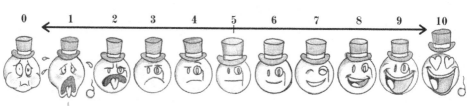

0   1   2   3   4   5   6   7   8   9   10

Brand: _____

Flavor: _____

Flavor Type:

Sweet   Tart/Sour   Herbal   Bitter   Spicy

Flavor Strength:

├─────────────┼─────────────┤
Too Weak   Just Right   Too Strong

Notes: Date: ___/___/___

Caffeine: Y N

SODA CHARACTERISTICS	SCORE
Bottle Shape, Style, & Color	
Labeling Aesthetics & Description	
Aroma & Drink Color	
Carbonation / Fizziness	
Drinkability / Refreshment	
Tastes as Advertised & Expected	
Overall Flavor	
Aftertaste / Finish	
Memorability	
Value for Price	
BOTTLECAP SCORE	

Brand: _____

Flavor: _____

Flavor Type:				
Sweet	Tart/Sour	Herbal	Bitter	Spicy

Flavor Strength:

Too Weak   Just Right   Too Strong

Notes: Date: ___/___/___

Caffeine: Y N

SODA CHARACTERISTICS	SCORE
Bottle Shape, Style, & Color	
Labeling Aesthetics & Description	
Aroma & Drink Color	
Carbonation / Fizziness	
Drinkability / Refreshment	
Tastes as Advertised & Expected	
Overall Flavor	
Aftertaste / Finish	
Memorability	
Value for Price	
BOTTLECAP SCORE	

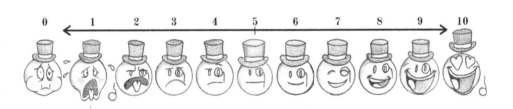

0   1   2   3   4   5   6   7   8   9   10

Brand: _____

Flavor: _____

Flavor Type:				
Sweet	Tart/Sour	Herbal	Bitter	Spicy

Flavor Strength:

Too Weak   Just Right   Too Strong

Notes: Date: ___/___/___

Caffeine: Y N

SODA CHARACTERISTICS	SCORE
Bottle Shape, Style, & Color	
Labeling Aesthetics & Description	
Aroma & Drink Color	
Carbonation / Fizziness	
Drinkability / Refreshment	
Tastes as Advertised & Expected	
Overall Flavor	
Aftertaste / Finish	
Memorability	
Value for Price	
BOTTLECAP SCORE	

Brand: _____

Flavor: _____

Flavor Type:

Sweet   Tart/Sour   Herbal   Bitter   Spicy

Flavor Strength:

Too Weak   Just Right   Too Strong

Notes: Date: ___/___/___

Caffeine: Y N

SODA CHARACTERISTICS	SCORE
Bottle Shape, Style, & Color	
Labeling Aesthetics & Description	
Aroma & Drink Color	
Carbonation / Fizziness	
Drinkability / Refreshment	
Tastes as Advertised & Expected	
Overall Flavor	
Aftertaste / Finish	
Memorability	
Value for Price	
BOTTLECAP SCORE	

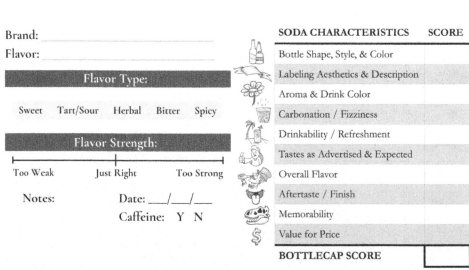

0   1   2   3   4   5   6   7   8   9   10

Brand: _____

Flavor: _____

Flavor Type:

Sweet   Tart/Sour   Herbal   Bitter   Spicy

Flavor Strength:

Too Weak   Just Right   Too Strong

Notes: Date: ___/___/___

Caffeine: Y N

SODA CHARACTERISTICS	SCORE
Bottle Shape, Style, & Color	
Labeling Aesthetics & Description	
Aroma & Drink Color	
Carbonation / Fizziness	
Drinkability / Refreshment	
Tastes as Advertised & Expected	
Overall Flavor	
Aftertaste / Finish	
Memorability	
Value for Price	
BOTTLECAP SCORE	

Brand: _____

Flavor: _____

Flavor Type:				
Sweet	Tart/Sour	Herbal	Bitter	Spicy

Flavor Strength:

Too Weak   Just Right   Too Strong

Notes: Date: ___/___/___

Caffeine: Y   N

SODA CHARACTERISTICS	SCORE
Bottle Shape, Style, & Color	
Labeling Aesthetics & Description	
Aroma & Drink Color	
Carbonation / Fizziness	
Drinkability / Refreshment	
Tastes as Advertised & Expected	
Overall Flavor	
Aftertaste / Finish	
Memorability	
Value for Price	
BOTTLECAP SCORE	

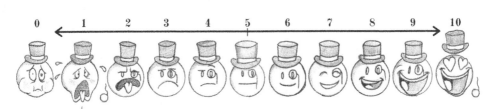

0   1   2   3   4   5   6   7   8   9   10

Brand: _____

Flavor: _____

Flavor Type:				
Sweet	Tart/Sour	Herbal	Bitter	Spicy

Flavor Strength:

Too Weak   Just Right   Too Strong

Notes: Date: ___/___/___

Caffeine: Y   N

SODA CHARACTERISTICS	SCORE
Bottle Shape, Style, & Color	
Labeling Aesthetics & Description	
Aroma & Drink Color	
Carbonation / Fizziness	
Drinkability / Refreshment	
Tastes as Advertised & Expected	
Overall Flavor	
Aftertaste / Finish	
Memorability	
Value for Price	
BOTTLECAP SCORE	

Brand: _____

Flavor: _____

Flavor Type:

Sweet   Tart/Sour   Herbal   Bitter   Spicy

Flavor Strength:

Too Weak   Just Right   Too Strong

Notes: Date: ___/___/___

Caffeine: Y N

SODA CHARACTERISTICS	SCORE
Bottle Shape, Style, & Color	
Labeling Aesthetics & Description	
Aroma & Drink Color	
Carbonation / Fizziness	
Drinkability / Refreshment	
Tastes as Advertised & Expected	
Overall Flavor	
Aftertaste / Finish	
Memorability	
Value for Price	
BOTTLECAP SCORE	

Brand: _____

Flavor: _____

Flavor Type:

Sweet   Tart/Sour   Herbal   Bitter   Spicy

Flavor Strength:

Too Weak   Just Right   Too Strong

Notes: Date: ___/___/___

Caffeine: Y N

SODA CHARACTERISTICS	SCORE
Bottle Shape, Style, & Color	
Labeling Aesthetics & Description	
Aroma & Drink Color	
Carbonation / Fizziness	
Drinkability / Refreshment	
Tastes as Advertised & Expected	
Overall Flavor	
Aftertaste / Finish	
Memorability	
Value for Price	
BOTTLECAP SCORE	

Brand: _____

Flavor: _____

Flavor Type:

Sweet   Tart/Sour   Herbal   Bitter   Spicy

Flavor Strength:

Too Weak   Just Right   Too Strong

Notes: Date: ___/___/___

Caffeine: Y N

SODA CHARACTERISTICS	SCORE
Bottle Shape, Style, & Color	
Labeling Aesthetics & Description	
Aroma & Drink Color	
Carbonation / Fizziness	
Drinkability / Refreshment	
Tastes as Advertised & Expected	
Overall Flavor	
Aftertaste / Finish	
Memorability	
Value for Price	
BOTTLECAP SCORE	

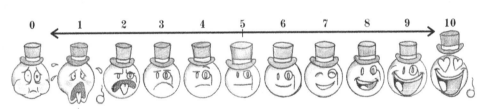

0   1   2   3   4   5   6   7   8   9   10

Brand: _____

Flavor: _____

Flavor Type:

Sweet   Tart/Sour   Herbal   Bitter   Spicy

Flavor Strength:

Too Weak   Just Right   Too Strong

Notes: Date: ___/___/___

Caffeine: Y N

SODA CHARACTERISTICS	SCORE
Bottle Shape, Style, & Color	
Labeling Aesthetics & Description	
Aroma & Drink Color	
Carbonation / Fizziness	
Drinkability / Refreshment	
Tastes as Advertised & Expected	
Overall Flavor	
Aftertaste / Finish	
Memorability	
Value for Price	
BOTTLECAP SCORE	

Brand: _____

Flavor: _____

Flavor Type:

Sweet   Tart/Sour   Herbal   Bitter   Spicy

Flavor Strength:

Too Weak   Just Right   Too Strong

Notes: Date: ___/___/___

Caffeine: Y N

SODA CHARACTERISTICS	SCORE
Bottle Shape, Style, & Color	
Labeling Aesthetics & Description	
Aroma & Drink Color	
Carbonation / Fizziness	
Drinkability / Refreshment	
Tastes as Advertised & Expected	
Overall Flavor	
Aftertaste / Finish	
Memorability	
Value for Price	
BOTTLECAP SCORE	

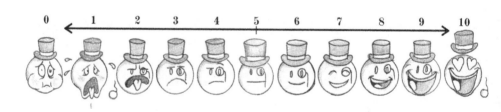

Brand: _____

Flavor: _____

Flavor Type:

Sweet   Tart/Sour   Herbal   Bitter   Spicy

Flavor Strength:

Too Weak   Just Right   Too Strong

Notes: Date: ___/___/___

Caffeine: Y N

SODA CHARACTERISTICS	SCORE
Bottle Shape, Style, & Color	
Labeling Aesthetics & Description	
Aroma & Drink Color	
Carbonation / Fizziness	
Drinkability / Refreshment	
Tastes as Advertised & Expected	
Overall Flavor	
Aftertaste / Finish	
Memorability	
Value for Price	
BOTTLECAP SCORE	

Brand: _____

Flavor: _____

Flavor Type:

Sweet   Tart/Sour   Herbal   Bitter   Spicy

Flavor Strength:

Too Weak   Just Right   Too Strong

Notes: Date: ___/___/___

Caffeine: Y   N

SODA CHARACTERISTICS	SCORE
Bottle Shape, Style, & Color	
Labeling Aesthetics & Description	
Aroma & Drink Color	
Carbonation / Fizziness	
Drinkability / Refreshment	
Tastes as Advertised & Expected	
Overall Flavor	
Aftertaste / Finish	
Memorability	
Value for Price	
BOTTLECAP SCORE	

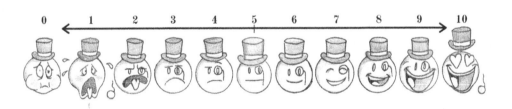

0   1   2   3   4   5   6   7   8   9   10

Brand: _____

Flavor: _____

Flavor Type:

Sweet   Tart/Sour   Herbal   Bitter   Spicy

Flavor Strength:

Too Weak   Just Right   Too Strong

Notes: Date: ___/___/___

Caffeine: Y   N

SODA CHARACTERISTICS	SCORE
Bottle Shape, Style, & Color	
Labeling Aesthetics & Description	
Aroma & Drink Color	
Carbonation / Fizziness	
Drinkability / Refreshment	
Tastes as Advertised & Expected	
Overall Flavor	
Aftertaste / Finish	
Memorability	
Value for Price	
BOTTLECAP SCORE	

Brand: _____

Flavor: _____

Flavor Type:

Sweet   Tart/Sour   Herbal   Bitter   Spicy

Flavor Strength:

Too Weak   Just Right   Too Strong

Notes: Date: ___/___/___

Caffeine: Y   N

SODA CHARACTERISTICS	SCORE
Bottle Shape, Style, & Color	
Labeling Aesthetics & Description	
Aroma & Drink Color	
Carbonation / Fizziness	
Drinkability / Refreshment	
Tastes as Advertised & Expected	
Overall Flavor	
Aftertaste / Finish	
Memorability	
Value for Price	
BOTTLECAP SCORE	

Brand: _____

Flavor: _____

Flavor Type:

Sweet   Tart/Sour   Herbal   Bitter   Spicy

Flavor Strength:

Too Weak   Just Right   Too Strong

Notes: Date: ___/___/___

Caffeine: Y   N

SODA CHARACTERISTICS	SCORE
Bottle Shape, Style, & Color	
Labeling Aesthetics & Description	
Aroma & Drink Color	
Carbonation / Fizziness	
Drinkability / Refreshment	
Tastes as Advertised & Expected	
Overall Flavor	
Aftertaste / Finish	
Memorability	
Value for Price	
BOTTLECAP SCORE	

Brand: _____

Flavor: _____

Flavor Type:				
Sweet	Tart/Sour	Herbal	Bitter	Spicy

Flavor Strength:

Too Weak   Just Right   Too Strong

Notes: Date: ___/___/___

Caffeine: Y N

SODA CHARACTERISTICS	SCORE
Bottle Shape, Style, & Color	
Labeling Aesthetics & Description	
Aroma & Drink Color	
Carbonation / Fizziness	
Drinkability / Refreshment	
Tastes as Advertised & Expected	
Overall Flavor	
Aftertaste / Finish	
Memorability	
Value for Price	
BOTTLECAP SCORE	

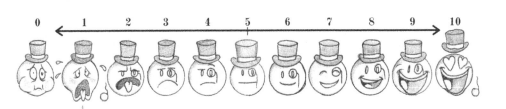

0   1   2   3   4   5   6   7   8   9   10

Brand: _____

Flavor: _____

Flavor Type:				
Sweet	Tart/Sour	Herbal	Bitter	Spicy

Flavor Strength:

Too Weak   Just Right   Too Strong

Notes: Date: ___/___/___

Caffeine: Y N

SODA CHARACTERISTICS	SCORE
Bottle Shape, Style, & Color	
Labeling Aesthetics & Description	
Aroma & Drink Color	
Carbonation / Fizziness	
Drinkability / Refreshment	
Tastes as Advertised & Expected	
Overall Flavor	
Aftertaste / Finish	
Memorability	
Value for Price	
BOTTLECAP SCORE	

Brand: _____

Flavor: _____

Flavor Type:				
Sweet	Tart/Sour	Herbal	Bitter	Spicy

Flavor Strength:

Too Weak   Just Right   Too Strong

Notes:

Date: ___/___/___

Caffeine: Y N

SODA CHARACTERISTICS	SCORE
Bottle Shape, Style, & Color	
Labeling Aesthetics & Description	
Aroma & Drink Color	
Carbonation / Fizziness	
Drinkability / Refreshment	
Tastes as Advertised & Expected	
Overall Flavor	
Aftertaste / Finish	
Memorability	
Value for Price	
BOTTLECAP SCORE	

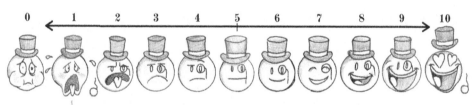

Brand: _____

Flavor: _____

Flavor Type:				
Sweet	Tart/Sour	Herbal	Bitter	Spicy

Flavor Strength:

Too Weak   Just Right   Too Strong

Notes:

Date: ___/___/___

Caffeine: Y N

SODA CHARACTERISTICS	SCORE
Bottle Shape, Style, & Color	
Labeling Aesthetics & Description	
Aroma & Drink Color	
Carbonation / Fizziness	
Drinkability / Refreshment	
Tastes as Advertised & Expected	
Overall Flavor	
Aftertaste / Finish	
Memorability	
Value for Price	
BOTTLECAP SCORE	

Brand: _____

Flavor: _____

Flavor Type:

Sweet   Tart/Sour   Herbal   Bitter   Spicy

Flavor Strength:

Too Weak   Just Right   Too Strong

Notes: Date: ___/___/___

Caffeine: Y N

SODA CHARACTERISTICS	SCORE
Bottle Shape, Style, & Color	
Labeling Aesthetics & Description	
Aroma & Drink Color	
Carbonation / Fizziness	
Drinkability / Refreshment	
Tastes as Advertised & Expected	
Overall Flavor	
Aftertaste / Finish	
Memorability	
Value for Price	
BOTTLECAP SCORE	

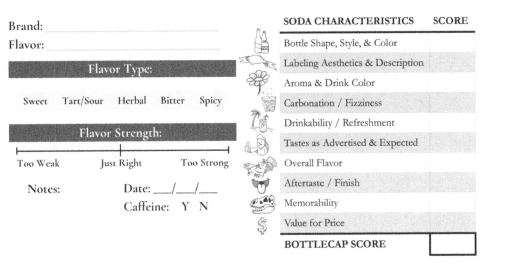

0   1   2   3   4   5   6   7   8   9   10

Brand: _____

Flavor: _____

Flavor Type:

Sweet   Tart/Sour   Herbal   Bitter   Spicy

Flavor Strength:

Too Weak   Just Right   Too Strong

Notes: Date: ___/___/___

Caffeine: Y N

SODA CHARACTERISTICS	SCORE
Bottle Shape, Style, & Color	
Labeling Aesthetics & Description	
Aroma & Drink Color	
Carbonation / Fizziness	
Drinkability / Refreshment	
Tastes as Advertised & Expected	
Overall Flavor	
Aftertaste / Finish	
Memorability	
Value for Price	
BOTTLECAP SCORE	

ROOT BEER & SARSAPARILLA FLAVORS

Brand	Flavor	Score	Notes	Page
				195
				195
				196
				196
				197
				197
				198
				198
				199
				199
				200
				200
				201
				201
				202
				202
				203
				203
				204
				204
				205
				205
				206
				206
				207
				207

Brand: _____

Flavor: _____

Flavor Type:

Sweet   Tart/Sour   Herbal   Bitter   Spicy

Flavor Strength:

Too Weak   Just Right   Too Strong

Notes: Date: ___/___/___

Caffeine: Y N

SODA CHARACTERISTICS	SCORE
Bottle Shape, Style, & Color	
Labeling Aesthetics & Description	
Aroma & Drink Color	
Carbonation / Fizziness	
Drinkability / Refreshment	
Tastes as Advertised & Expected	
Overall Flavor	
Aftertaste / Finish	
Memorability	
Value for Price	
BOTTLECAP SCORE	

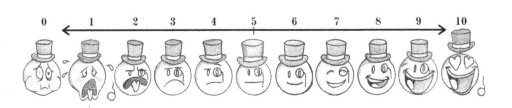

0 1 2 3 4 5 6 7 8 9 10

Brand: _____

Flavor: _____

Flavor Type:

Sweet   Tart/Sour   Herbal   Bitter   Spicy

Flavor Strength:

Too Weak   Just Right   Too Strong

Notes: Date: ___/___/___

Caffeine: Y N

SODA CHARACTERISTICS	SCORE
Bottle Shape, Style, & Color	
Labeling Aesthetics & Description	
Aroma & Drink Color	
Carbonation / Fizziness	
Drinkability / Refreshment	
Tastes as Advertised & Expected	
Overall Flavor	
Aftertaste / Finish	
Memorability	
Value for Price	
BOTTLECAP SCORE	

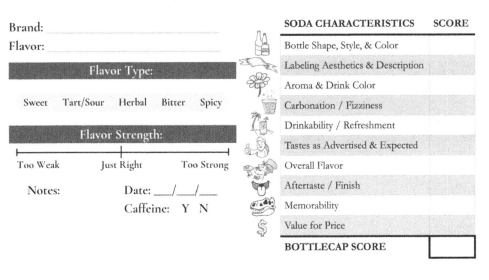

Brand: _____

Flavor: _____

Flavor Type:

Sweet   Tart/Sour   Herbal   Bitter   Spicy

Flavor Strength:

Too Weak   Just Right   Too Strong

Notes: Date: ___/___/___

Caffeine: Y N

SODA CHARACTERISTICS	SCORE
Bottle Shape, Style, & Color	
Labeling Aesthetics & Description	
Aroma & Drink Color	
Carbonation / Fizziness	
Drinkability / Refreshment	
Tastes as Advertised & Expected	
Overall Flavor	
Aftertaste / Finish	
Memorability	
Value for Price	
BOTTLECAP SCORE	

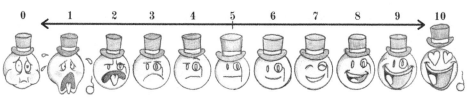

0   1   2   3   4   5   6   7   8   9   10

Brand: _____

Flavor: _____

Flavor Type:

Sweet   Tart/Sour   Herbal   Bitter   Spicy

Flavor Strength:

Too Weak   Just Right   Too Strong

Notes: Date: ___/___/___

Caffeine: Y N

SODA CHARACTERISTICS	SCORE
Bottle Shape, Style, & Color	
Labeling Aesthetics & Description	
Aroma & Drink Color	
Carbonation / Fizziness	
Drinkability / Refreshment	
Tastes as Advertised & Expected	
Overall Flavor	
Aftertaste / Finish	
Memorability	
Value for Price	
BOTTLECAP SCORE	

Brand: _____

Flavor: _____

Flavor Type:

Sweet   Tart/Sour   Herbal   Bitter   Spicy

Flavor Strength:

Too Weak   Just Right   Too Strong

Notes: Date: ___/___/___

                    Caffeine: Y N

SODA CHARACTERISTICS	SCORE
Bottle Shape, Style, & Color	
Labeling Aesthetics & Description	
Aroma & Drink Color	
Carbonation / Fizziness	
Drinkability / Refreshment	
Tastes as Advertised & Expected	
Overall Flavor	
Aftertaste / Finish	
Memorability	
Value for Price	
BOTTLECAP SCORE	

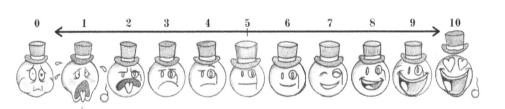

0   1   2   3   4   5   6   7   8   9   10

Brand: _____

Flavor: _____

Flavor Type:

Sweet   Tart/Sour   Herbal   Bitter   Spicy

Flavor Strength:

Too Weak   Just Right   Too Strong

Notes: Date: ___/___/___

                    Caffeine: Y N

SODA CHARACTERISTICS	SCORE
Bottle Shape, Style, & Color	
Labeling Aesthetics & Description	
Aroma & Drink Color	
Carbonation / Fizziness	
Drinkability / Refreshment	
Tastes as Advertised & Expected	
Overall Flavor	
Aftertaste / Finish	
Memorability	
Value for Price	
BOTTLECAP SCORE	

Brand: _____

Flavor: _____

Flavor Type:

Sweet   Tart/Sour   Herbal   Bitter   Spicy

Flavor Strength:

Too Weak   Just Right   Too Strong

Notes: Date: ___/___/___

                  Caffeine: Y N

SODA CHARACTERISTICS	SCORE
Bottle Shape, Style, & Color	
Labeling Aesthetics & Description	
Aroma & Drink Color	
Carbonation / Fizziness	
Drinkability / Refreshment	
Tastes as Advertised & Expected	
Overall Flavor	
Aftertaste / Finish	
Memorability	
Value for Price	
BOTTLECAP SCORE	

0   1   2   3   4   5   6   7   8   9   10

Brand: _____

Flavor: _____

Flavor Type:

Sweet   Tart/Sour   Herbal   Bitter   Spicy

Flavor Strength:

Too Weak   Just Right   Too Strong

Notes: Date: ___/___/___

                  Caffeine: Y N

SODA CHARACTERISTICS	SCORE
Bottle Shape, Style, & Color	
Labeling Aesthetics & Description	
Aroma & Drink Color	
Carbonation / Fizziness	
Drinkability / Refreshment	
Tastes as Advertised & Expected	
Overall Flavor	
Aftertaste / Finish	
Memorability	
Value for Price	
BOTTLECAP SCORE	

Brand: _____

Flavor: _____

Flavor Type:

Sweet   Tart/Sour   Herbal   Bitter   Spicy

Flavor Strength:

Too Weak   Just Right   Too Strong

Notes: Date: ___/___/___

Caffeine: Y N

SODA CHARACTERISTICS	SCORE
Bottle Shape, Style, & Color	
Labeling Aesthetics & Description	
Aroma & Drink Color	
Carbonation / Fizziness	
Drinkability / Refreshment	
Tastes as Advertised & Expected	
Overall Flavor	
Aftertaste / Finish	
Memorability	
Value for Price	
BOTTLECAP SCORE	

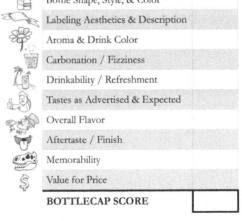

0   1   2   3   4   5   6   7   8   9   10

Brand: _____

Flavor: _____

Flavor Type:

Sweet   Tart/Sour   Herbal   Bitter   Spicy

Flavor Strength:

Too Weak   Just Right   Too Strong

Notes: Date: ___/___/___

Caffeine: Y N

SODA CHARACTERISTICS	SCORE
Bottle Shape, Style, & Color	
Labeling Aesthetics & Description	
Aroma & Drink Color	
Carbonation / Fizziness	
Drinkability / Refreshment	
Tastes as Advertised & Expected	
Overall Flavor	
Aftertaste / Finish	
Memorability	
Value for Price	
BOTTLECAP SCORE	

Brand: _____

Flavor: _____

Flavor Type:

Sweet   Tart/Sour   Herbal   Bitter   Spicy

Flavor Strength:

Too Weak   Just Right   Too Strong

Notes: Date: ___/___/___

Caffeine: Y N

SODA CHARACTERISTICS	SCORE
Bottle Shape, Style, & Color	
Labeling Aesthetics & Description	
Aroma & Drink Color	
Carbonation / Fizziness	
Drinkability / Refreshment	
Tastes as Advertised & Expected	
Overall Flavor	
Aftertaste / Finish	
Memorability	
Value for Price	
BOTTLECAP SCORE	

0   1   2   3   4   5   6   7   8   9   10

Brand: _____

Flavor: _____

Flavor Type:

Sweet   Tart/Sour   Herbal   Bitter   Spicy

Flavor Strength:

Too Weak   Just Right   Too Strong

Notes: Date: ___/___/___

Caffeine: Y N

SODA CHARACTERISTICS	SCORE
Bottle Shape, Style, & Color	
Labeling Aesthetics & Description	
Aroma & Drink Color	
Carbonation / Fizziness	
Drinkability / Refreshment	
Tastes as Advertised & Expected	
Overall Flavor	
Aftertaste / Finish	
Memorability	
Value for Price	
BOTTLECAP SCORE	

Brand: _____

Flavor: _____

Flavor Type:				
Sweet	Tart/Sour	Herbal	Bitter	Spicy

Flavor Strength:

Too Weak — Just Right — Too Strong

Notes:

Date: ___/___/___

Caffeine: Y N

SODA CHARACTERISTICS	SCORE
Bottle Shape, Style, & Color	
Labeling Aesthetics & Description	
Aroma & Drink Color	
Carbonation / Fizziness	
Drinkability / Refreshment	
Tastes as Advertised & Expected	
Overall Flavor	
Aftertaste / Finish	
Memorability	
Value for Price	
BOTTLECAP SCORE	

0   1   2   3   4   5   6   7   8   9   10

Brand: _____

Flavor: _____

Flavor Type:				
Sweet	Tart/Sour	Herbal	Bitter	Spicy

Flavor Strength:

Too Weak — Just Right — Too Strong

Notes:

Date: ___/___/___

· Caffeine: Y N

SODA CHARACTERISTICS	SCORE
Bottle Shape, Style, & Color	
Labeling Aesthetics & Description	
Aroma & Drink Color	
Carbonation / Fizziness	
Drinkability / Refreshment	
Tastes as Advertised & Expected	
Overall Flavor	
Aftertaste / Finish	
Memorability	
Value for Price	
BOTTLECAP SCORE	

Brand: _____

Flavor: _____

Flavor Type:

Sweet   Tart/Sour   Herbal   Bitter   Spicy

Flavor Strength:

Too Weak   Just Right   Too Strong

Notes: Date: ___/___/___

Caffeine: Y N

SODA CHARACTERISTICS	SCORE
Bottle Shape, Style, & Color	
Labeling Aesthetics & Description	
Aroma & Drink Color	
Carbonation / Fizziness	
Drinkability / Refreshment	
Tastes as Advertised & Expected	
Overall Flavor	
Aftertaste / Finish	
Memorability	
Value for Price	
BOTTLECAP SCORE	

0 1 2 3 4 5 6 7 8 9 10

Brand: _____

Flavor: _____

Flavor Type:

Sweet   Tart/Sour   Herbal   Bitter   Spicy

Flavor Strength:

Too Weak   Just Right   Too Strong

Notes: Date: ___/___/___

Caffeine: Y N

SODA CHARACTERISTICS	SCORE
Bottle Shape, Style, & Color	
Labeling Aesthetics & Description	
Aroma & Drink Color	
Carbonation / Fizziness	
Drinkability / Refreshment	
Tastes as Advertised & Expected	
Overall Flavor	
Aftertaste / Finish	
Memorability	
Value for Price	
BOTTLECAP SCORE	

Brand: _____

Flavor: _____

Flavor Type:

Sweet   Tart/Sour   Herbal   Bitter   Spicy

Flavor Strength:

Too Weak   Just Right   Too Strong

Notes: Date: ___/___/___

Caffeine: Y   N

SODA CHARACTERISTICS	SCORE
Bottle Shape, Style, & Color	
Labeling Aesthetics & Description	
Aroma & Drink Color	
Carbonation / Fizziness	
Drinkability / Refreshment	
Tastes as Advertised & Expected	
Overall Flavor	
Aftertaste / Finish	
Memorability	
Value for Price	
BOTTLECAP SCORE	

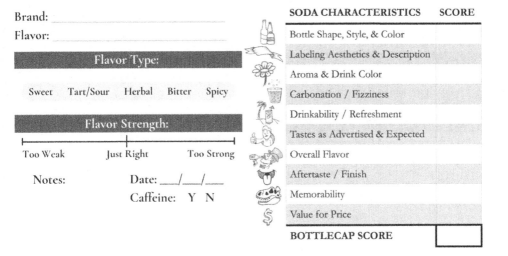

0   1   2   3   4   5   6   7   8   9   10

Brand: _____

Flavor: _____

Flavor Type:

Sweet   Tart/Sour   Herbal   Bitter   Spicy

Flavor Strength:

Too Weak   Just Right   Too Strong

Notes: Date: ___/___/___

Caffeine: Y   N

SODA CHARACTERISTICS	SCORE
Bottle Shape, Style, & Color	
Labeling Aesthetics & Description	
Aroma & Drink Color	
Carbonation / Fizziness	
Drinkability / Refreshment	
Tastes as Advertised & Expected	
Overall Flavor	
Aftertaste / Finish	
Memorability	
Value for Price	
BOTTLECAP SCORE	

Brand: _____

Flavor: _____

Flavor Type:

Sweet   Tart/Sour   Herbal   Bitter   Spicy

Flavor Strength:

Too Weak   Just Right   Too Strong

Notes: Date: ___/___/___

Caffeine: Y N

SODA CHARACTERISTICS	SCORE
Bottle Shape, Style, & Color	
Labeling Aesthetics & Description	
Aroma & Drink Color	
Carbonation / Fizziness	
Drinkability / Refreshment	
Tastes as Advertised & Expected	
Overall Flavor	
Aftertaste / Finish	
Memorability	
Value for Price	
BOTTLECAP SCORE	

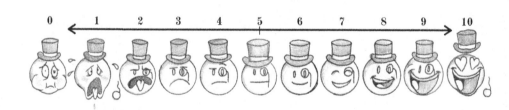

0   1   2   3   4   5   6   7   8   9   10

Brand: _____

Flavor: _____

Flavor Type:

Sweet   Tart/Sour   Herbal   Bitter   Spicy

Flavor Strength:

Too Weak   Just Right   Too Strong

Notes: Date: ___/___/___

Caffeine: Y N

SODA CHARACTERISTICS	SCORE
Bottle Shape, Style, & Color	
Labeling Aesthetics & Description	
Aroma & Drink Color	
Carbonation / Fizziness	
Drinkability / Refreshment	
Tastes as Advertised & Expected	
Overall Flavor	
Aftertaste / Finish	
Memorability	
Value for Price	
BOTTLECAP SCORE	

ROOT BEER & SARSAPARILLA FLAVORS

Brand: _____
Flavor: _____

Flavor Type:

Sweet   Tart/Sour   Herbal   Bitter   Spicy

Flavor Strength:

Too Weak   Just Right   Too Strong

Notes: Date: ___/___/___
              Caffeine: Y N

SODA CHARACTERISTICS	SCORE
Bottle Shape, Style, & Color	
Labeling Aesthetics & Description	
Aroma & Drink Color	
Carbonation / Fizziness	
Drinkability / Refreshment	
Tastes as Advertised & Expected	
Overall Flavor	
Aftertaste / Finish	
Memorability	
Value for Price	
BOTTLECAP SCORE	

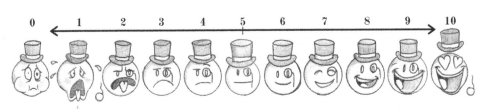

0   1   2   3   4   5   6   7   8   9   10

Brand: _____
Flavor: _____

Flavor Type:

Sweet   Tart/Sour   Herbal   Bitter   Spicy

Flavor Strength:

Too Weak   Just Right   Too Strong

Notes: Date: ___/___/___
              Caffeine: Y N

SODA CHARACTERISTICS	SCORE
Bottle Shape, Style, & Color	
Labeling Aesthetics & Description	
Aroma & Drink Color	
Carbonation / Fizziness	
Drinkability / Refreshment	
Tastes as Advertised & Expected	
Overall Flavor	
Aftertaste / Finish	
Memorability	
Value for Price	
BOTTLECAP SCORE	

Brand: _____

Flavor: _____

Flavor Type:

Sweet   Tart/Sour   Herbal   Bitter   Spicy

Flavor Strength:

Too Weak   Just Right   Too Strong

Notes: Date: ___/___/___

Caffeine: Y N

SODA CHARACTERISTICS	SCORE
Bottle Shape, Style, & Color	
Labeling Aesthetics & Description	
Aroma & Drink Color	
Carbonation / Fizziness	
Drinkability / Refreshment	
Tastes as Advertised & Expected	
Overall Flavor	
Aftertaste / Finish	
Memorability	
Value for Price	
BOTTLECAP SCORE	

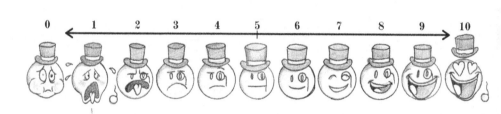

0   1   2   3   4   5   6   7   8   9   10

Brand: _____

Flavor: _____

Flavor Type:

Sweet   Tart/Sour   Herbal   Bitter   Spicy

Flavor Strength:

Too Weak   Just Right   Too Strong

Notes: Date: ___/___/___

Caffeine: Y N

SODA CHARACTERISTICS	SCORE
Bottle Shape, Style, & Color	
Labeling Aesthetics & Description	
Aroma & Drink Color	
Carbonation / Fizziness	
Drinkability / Refreshment	
Tastes as Advertised & Expected	
Overall Flavor	
Aftertaste / Finish	
Memorability	
Value for Price	
BOTTLECAP SCORE	

Brand: _____

Flavor: _____

Flavor Type:

Sweet   Tart/Sour   Herbal   Bitter   Spicy

Flavor Strength:

Too Weak   Just Right   Too Strong

Notes: Date: ___/___/___

Caffeine: Y   N

SODA CHARACTERISTICS	SCORE
Bottle Shape, Style, & Color	
Labeling Aesthetics & Description	
Aroma & Drink Color	
Carbonation / Fizziness	
Drinkability / Refreshment	
Tastes as Advertised & Expected	
Overall Flavor	
Aftertaste / Finish	
Memorability	
Value for Price	
BOTTLECAP SCORE	

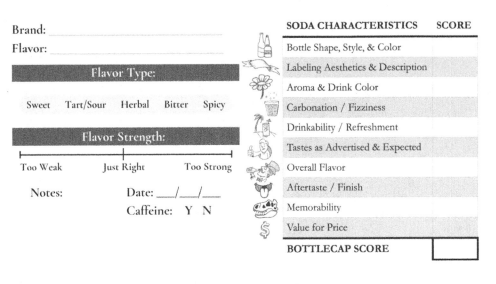

Brand: _____

Flavor: _____

Flavor Type:

Sweet   Tart/Sour   Herbal   Bitter   Spicy

Flavor Strength:

Too Weak   Just Right   Too Strong

Notes: Date: ___/___/___

Caffeine: Y   N

SODA CHARACTERISTICS	SCORE
Bottle Shape, Style, & Color	
Labeling Aesthetics & Description	
Aroma & Drink Color	
Carbonation / Fizziness	
Drinkability / Refreshment	
Tastes as Advertised & Expected	
Overall Flavor	
Aftertaste / Finish	
Memorability	
Value for Price	
BOTTLECAP SCORE	

UNUSUAL & EXOTIC FLAVORS

Brand	Flavor	Score	Notes	Page
				209
				209
				210
				210
				211
				211
				212
				212
				213
				213
				214
				214
				215
				215
				216
				216
				217
				217
				218
				218
				219
				219
				220
				220
				221
				221

Brand: _____

Flavor: _____

Flavor Type:

Sweet   Tart/Sour   Herbal   Bitter   Spicy

Flavor Strength:

Too Weak   Just Right   Too Strong

Notes: Date: ___/___/___

Caffeine: Y   N

SODA CHARACTERISTICS	SCORE
Bottle Shape, Style, & Color	
Labeling Aesthetics & Description	
Aroma & Drink Color	
Carbonation / Fizziness	
Drinkability / Refreshment	
Tastes as Advertised & Expected	
Overall Flavor	
Aftertaste / Finish	
Memorability	
Value for Price	
BOTTLECAP SCORE	

0   1   2   3   4   5   6   7   8   9   10

Brand: _____

Flavor: _____

Flavor Type:

Sweet   Tart/Sour   Herbal   Bitter   Spicy

Flavor Strength:

Too Weak   Just Right   Too Strong

Notes: Date: ___/___/___

Caffeine: Y   N

SODA CHARACTERISTICS	SCORE
Bottle Shape, Style, & Color	
Labeling Aesthetics & Description	
Aroma & Drink Color	
Carbonation / Fizziness	
Drinkability / Refreshment	
Tastes as Advertised & Expected	
Overall Flavor	
Aftertaste / Finish	
Memorability	
Value for Price	
BOTTLECAP SCORE	

Brand: _____

Flavor: _____

Flavor Type:

Sweet   Tart/Sour   Herbal   Bitter   Spicy

Flavor Strength:

Too Weak   Just Right   Too Strong

Notes: Date: ___/___/___

Caffeine: Y N

SODA CHARACTERISTICS	SCORE
Bottle Shape, Style, & Color	
Labeling Aesthetics & Description	
Aroma & Drink Color	
Carbonation / Fizziness	
Drinkability / Refreshment	
Tastes as Advertised & Expected	
Overall Flavor	
Aftertaste / Finish	
Memorability	
Value for Price	
BOTTLECAP SCORE	

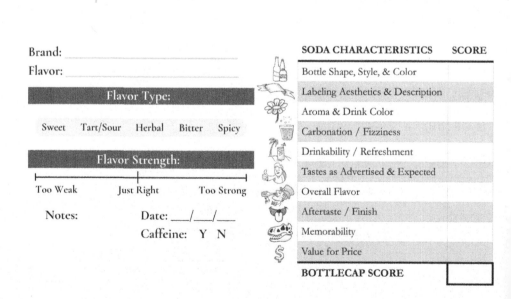

0   1   2   3   4   5   6   7   8   9   10

Brand: _____

Flavor: _____

Flavor Type:

Sweet   Tart/Sour   Herbal   Bitter   Spicy

Flavor Strength:

Too Weak   Just Right   Too Strong

Notes: Date: ___/___/___

Caffeine: Y N

SODA CHARACTERISTICS	SCORE
Bottle Shape, Style, & Color	
Labeling Aesthetics & Description	
Aroma & Drink Color	
Carbonation / Fizziness	
Drinkability / Refreshment	
Tastes as Advertised & Expected	
Overall Flavor	
Aftertaste / Finish	
Memorability	
Value for Price	
BOTTLECAP SCORE	

Brand: _____

Flavor: _____

Flavor Type:

Sweet   Tart/Sour   Herbal   Bitter   Spicy

Flavor Strength:

Too Weak   Just Right   Too Strong

Notes: Date: ___/___/___

Caffeine: Y N

SODA CHARACTERISTICS	SCORE
Bottle Shape, Style, & Color	
Labeling Aesthetics & Description	
Aroma & Drink Color	
Carbonation / Fizziness	
Drinkability / Refreshment	
Tastes as Advertised & Expected	
Overall Flavor	
Aftertaste / Finish	
Memorability	
Value for Price	
BOTTLECAP SCORE	

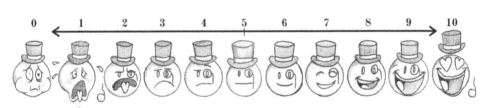

0 1 2 3 4 5 6 7 8 9 10

Brand: _____

Flavor: _____

Flavor Type:

Sweet   Tart/Sour   Herbal   Bitter   Spicy

Flavor Strength:

Too Weak   Just Right   Too Strong

Notes: Date: ___/___/___

Caffeine: Y N

SODA CHARACTERISTICS	SCORE
Bottle Shape, Style, & Color	
Labeling Aesthetics & Description	
Aroma & Drink Color	
Carbonation / Fizziness	
Drinkability / Refreshment	
Tastes as Advertised & Expected	
Overall Flavor	
Aftertaste / Finish	
Memorability	
Value for Price	
BOTTLECAP SCORE	

Brand: _____

Flavor: _____

Flavor Type:

Sweet   Tart/Sour   Herbal   Bitter   Spicy

Flavor Strength:

Too Weak   Just Right   Too Strong

Notes: Date: ___/___/___

Caffeine: Y   N

SODA CHARACTERISTICS	SCORE
Bottle Shape, Style, & Color	
Labeling Aesthetics & Description	
Aroma & Drink Color	
Carbonation / Fizziness	
Drinkability / Refreshment	
Tastes as Advertised & Expected	
Overall Flavor	
Aftertaste / Finish	
Memorability	
Value for Price	
BOTTLECAP SCORE	

Brand: _____

Flavor: _____

Flavor Type:

Sweet   Tart/Sour   Herbal   Bitter   Spicy

Flavor Strength:

Too Weak   Just Right   Too Strong

Notes: Date: ___/___/___

Caffeine: Y   N

SODA CHARACTERISTICS	SCORE
Bottle Shape, Style, & Color	
Labeling Aesthetics & Description	
Aroma & Drink Color	
Carbonation / Fizziness	
Drinkability / Refreshment	
Tastes as Advertised & Expected	
Overall Flavor	
Aftertaste / Finish	
Memorability	
Value for Price	
BOTTLECAP SCORE	

Brand: _____

Flavor: _____

Flavor Type:

Sweet   Tart/Sour   Herbal   Bitter   Spicy

Flavor Strength:

Too Weak   Just Right   Too Strong

Notes: Date: ___/___/___

Caffeine: Y N

SODA CHARACTERISTICS	SCORE
Bottle Shape, Style, & Color	
Labeling Aesthetics & Description	
Aroma & Drink Color	
Carbonation / Fizziness	
Drinkability / Refreshment	
Tastes as Advertised & Expected	
Overall Flavor	
Aftertaste / Finish	
Memorability	
Value for Price	
BOTTLECAP SCORE	

0   1   2   3   4   5   6   7   8   9   10

Brand: _____

Flavor: _____

Flavor Type:

Sweet   Tart/Sour   Herbal   Bitter   Spicy

Flavor Strength:

Too Weak   Just Right   Too Strong

Notes: Date: ___/___/___

Caffeine: Y N

SODA CHARACTERISTICS	SCORE
Bottle Shape, Style, & Color	
Labeling Aesthetics & Description	
Aroma & Drink Color	
Carbonation / Fizziness	
Drinkability / Refreshment	
Tastes as Advertised & Expected	
Overall Flavor	
Aftertaste / Finish	
Memorability	
Value for Price	
BOTTLECAP SCORE	

Brand: _____
Flavor: _____

Flavor Type:

Sweet   Tart/Sour   Herbal   Bitter   Spicy

Flavor Strength:

Too Weak   Just Right   Too Strong

Notes: Date: ___/___/___
              Caffeine: Y N

SODA CHARACTERISTICS	SCORE
Bottle Shape, Style, & Color	
Labeling Aesthetics & Description	
Aroma & Drink Color	
Carbonation / Fizziness	
Drinkability / Refreshment	
Tastes as Advertised & Expected	
Overall Flavor	
Aftertaste / Finish	
Memorability	
Value for Price	
BOTTLECAP SCORE	

0   1   2   3   4   5   6   7   8   9   10

Brand: _____
Flavor: _____

Flavor Type:

Sweet   Tart/Sour   Herbal   Bitter   Spicy

Flavor Strength:

Too Weak   Just Right   Too Strong

Notes: Date: ___/___/___
              Caffeine: Y N

SODA CHARACTERISTICS	SCORE
Bottle Shape, Style, & Color	
Labeling Aesthetics & Description	
Aroma & Drink Color	
Carbonation / Fizziness	
Drinkability / Refreshment	
Tastes as Advertised & Expected	
Overall Flavor	
Aftertaste / Finish	
Memorability	
Value for Price	
BOTTLECAP SCORE	

Brand: _____

Flavor: _____

Flavor Type:

Sweet   Tart/Sour   Herbal   Bitter   Spicy

Flavor Strength:

Too Weak   Just Right   Too Strong

Notes: Date: ___/___/___

Caffeine: Y N

SODA CHARACTERISTICS	SCORE
Bottle Shape, Style, & Color	
Labeling Aesthetics & Description	
Aroma & Drink Color	
Carbonation / Fizziness	
Drinkability / Refreshment	
Tastes as Advertised & Expected	
Overall Flavor	
Aftertaste / Finish	
Memorability	
Value for Price	
BOTTLECAP SCORE	

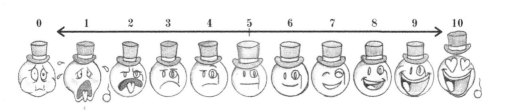

0   1   2   3   4   5   6   7   8   9   10

Brand: _____

Flavor: _____

Flavor Type:

Sweet   Tart/Sour   Herbal   Bitter   Spicy

Flavor Strength:

Too Weak   Just Right   Too Strong

Notes: Date: ___/___/___

Caffeine: Y N

SODA CHARACTERISTICS	SCORE
Bottle Shape, Style, & Color	
Labeling Aesthetics & Description	
Aroma & Drink Color	
Carbonation / Fizziness	
Drinkability / Refreshment	
Tastes as Advertised & Expected	
Overall Flavor	
Aftertaste / Finish	
Memorability	
Value for Price	
BOTTLECAP SCORE	

Brand: _____

Flavor: _____

Flavor Type:

Sweet   Tart/Sour   Herbal   Bitter   Spicy

Flavor Strength:

Too Weak   Just Right   Too Strong

Notes: Date: __/__/__

          Caffeine: Y N

SODA CHARACTERISTICS	SCORE
Bottle Shape, Style, & Color	
Labeling Aesthetics & Description	
Aroma & Drink Color	
Carbonation / Fizziness	
Drinkability / Refreshment	
Tastes as Advertised & Expected	
Overall Flavor	
Aftertaste / Finish	
Memorability	
Value for Price	
BOTTLECAP SCORE	

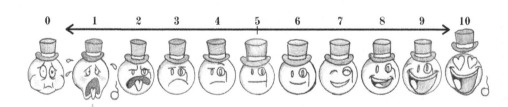

0   1   2   3   4   5   6   7   8   9   10

Brand: _____

Flavor: _____

Flavor Type:

Sweet   Tart/Sour   Herbal   Bitter   Spicy

Flavor Strength:

Too Weak   Just Right   Too Strong

Notes: Date: __/__/__

          Caffeine: Y N

SODA CHARACTERISTICS	SCORE
Bottle Shape, Style, & Color	
Labeling Aesthetics & Description	
Aroma & Drink Color	
Carbonation / Fizziness	
Drinkability / Refreshment	
Tastes as Advertised & Expected	
Overall Flavor	
Aftertaste / Finish	
Memorability	
Value for Price	
BOTTLECAP SCORE	

Brand: _____

Flavor: _____

SODA CHARACTERISTICS	SCORE
Bottle Shape, Style, & Color	
Labeling Aesthetics & Description	
Aroma & Drink Color	
Carbonation / Fizziness	
Drinkability / Refreshment	
Tastes as Advertised & Expected	
Overall Flavor	
Aftertaste / Finish	
Memorability	
Value for Price	
BOTTLECAP SCORE	

Flavor Type:

Sweet   Tart/Sour   Herbal   Bitter   Spicy

Flavor Strength:

Too Weak   Just Right   Too Strong

Notes: Date: ___/___/___

Caffeine: Y   N

0   1   2   3   4   5   6   7   8   9   10

Brand: _____

Flavor: _____

SODA CHARACTERISTICS	SCORE
Bottle Shape, Style, & Color	
Labeling Aesthetics & Description	
Aroma & Drink Color	
Carbonation / Fizziness	
Drinkability / Refreshment	
Tastes as Advertised & Expected	
Overall Flavor	
Aftertaste / Finish	
Memorability	
Value for Price	
BOTTLECAP SCORE	

Flavor Type:

Sweet   Tart/Sour   Herbal   Bitter   Spicy

Flavor Strength:

Too Weak   Just Right   Too Strong

Notes: Date: ___/___/___

Caffeine: Y   N

Brand: _____

Flavor: _____

Flavor Type:

Sweet   Tart/Sour   Herbal   Bitter   Spicy

Flavor Strength:

Too Weak   Just Right   Too Strong

Notes: Date: ___/___/___

Caffeine: Y   N

SODA CHARACTERISTICS	SCORE
Bottle Shape, Style, & Color	
Labeling Aesthetics & Description	
Aroma & Drink Color	
Carbonation / Fizziness	
Drinkability / Refreshment	
Tastes as Advertised & Expected	
Overall Flavor	
Aftertaste / Finish	
Memorability	
Value for Price	
BOTTLECAP SCORE	

0   1   2   3   4   5   6   7   8   9   10

Brand: _____

Flavor: _____

Flavor Type:

Sweet   Tart/Sour   Herbal   Bitter   Spicy

Flavor Strength:

Too Weak   Just Right   Too Strong

Notes: Date: ___/___/___

Caffeine: Y   N

SODA CHARACTERISTICS	SCORE
Bottle Shape, Style, & Color	
Labeling Aesthetics & Description	
Aroma & Drink Color	
Carbonation / Fizziness	
Drinkability / Refreshment	
Tastes as Advertised & Expected	
Overall Flavor	
Aftertaste / Finish	
Memorability	
Value for Price	
BOTTLECAP SCORE	

Brand: _____

Flavor: _____

Flavor Type:

Sweet   Tart/Sour   Herbal   Bitter   Spicy

Flavor Strength:

Too Weak   Just Right   Too Strong

Notes: Date: ___/___/___

Caffeine: Y N

SODA CHARACTERISTICS	SCORE
Bottle Shape, Style, & Color	
Labeling Aesthetics & Description	
Aroma & Drink Color	
Carbonation / Fizziness	
Drinkability / Refreshment	
Tastes as Advertised & Expected	
Overall Flavor	
Aftertaste / Finish	
Memorability	
Value for Price	
BOTTLECAP SCORE	

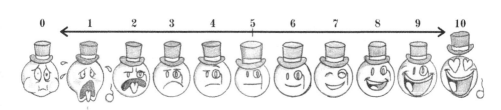

0   1   2   3   4   5   6   7   8   9   10

Brand: _____

Flavor: _____

Flavor Type:

Sweet   Tart/Sour   Herbal   Bitter   Spicy

Flavor Strength:

Too Weak   Just Right   Too Strong

Notes: Date: ___/___/___

Caffeine: Y N

SODA CHARACTERISTICS	SCORE
Bottle Shape, Style, & Color	
Labeling Aesthetics & Description	
Aroma & Drink Color	
Carbonation / Fizziness	
Drinkability / Refreshment	
Tastes as Advertised & Expected	
Overall Flavor	
Aftertaste / Finish	
Memorability	
Value for Price	
BOTTLECAP SCORE	

Brand: _____

Flavor: _____

Flavor Type:

Sweet   Tart/Sour   Herbal   Bitter   Spicy

Flavor Strength:

Too Weak   Just Right   Too Strong

Notes: Date: ___/___/___

Caffeine: Y N

SODA CHARACTERISTICS	SCORE
Bottle Shape, Style, & Color	
Labeling Aesthetics & Description	
Aroma & Drink Color	
Carbonation / Fizziness	
Drinkability / Refreshment	
Tastes as Advertised & Expected	
Overall Flavor	
Aftertaste / Finish	
Memorability	
Value for Price	
BOTTLECAP SCORE	

0 1 2 3 4 5 6 7 8 9 10

Brand: _____

Flavor: _____

Flavor Type:

Sweet   Tart/Sour   Herbal   Bitter   Spicy

Flavor Strength:

Too Weak   Just Right   Too Strong

Notes: Date: ___/___/___

Caffeine: Y N

SODA CHARACTERISTICS	SCORE
Bottle Shape, Style, & Color	
Labeling Aesthetics & Description	
Aroma & Drink Color	
Carbonation / Fizziness	
Drinkability / Refreshment	
Tastes as Advertised & Expected	
Overall Flavor	
Aftertaste / Finish	
Memorability	
Value for Price	
BOTTLECAP SCORE	

Brand: _____

Flavor: _____

Flavor Type:

Sweet   Tart/Sour   Herbal   Bitter   Spicy

Flavor Strength:

Too Weak   Just Right   Too Strong

Notes: Date: ___/___/___

Caffeine: Y N

SODA CHARACTERISTICS	SCORE
Bottle Shape, Style, & Color	
Labeling Aesthetics & Description	
Aroma & Drink Color	
Carbonation / Fizziness	
Drinkability / Refreshment	
Tastes as Advertised & Expected	
Overall Flavor	
Aftertaste / Finish	
Memorability	
Value for Price	
BOTTLECAP SCORE	

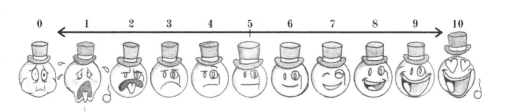

0   1   2   3   4   5   6   7   8   9   10

Brand: _____

Flavor: _____

Flavor Type:

Sweet   Tart/Sour   Herbal   Bitter   Spicy

Flavor Strength:

Too Weak   Just Right   Too Strong

Notes: Date: ___/___/___

Caffeine: Y N

SODA CHARACTERISTICS	SCORE
Bottle Shape, Style, & Color	
Labeling Aesthetics & Description	
Aroma & Drink Color	
Carbonation / Fizziness	
Drinkability / Refreshment	
Tastes as Advertised & Expected	
Overall Flavor	
Aftertaste / Finish	
Memorability	
Value for Price	
BOTTLECAP SCORE	

NOTES

Made in the USA
Monee, IL
25 September 2020